[handwritten inscription] Thank you for caring! Best wishes Judy B... Maria Nowicki

CAPS, CAPES, AND CARING:

The Legacy of Diploma Nursing Schools in Toledo

By Patricia Ringos Beach,
Susan J. Eisel, Maria Elizabeth Nowicki,
Judy Harris Szor, and Beth E. White

Introduction by Jodi S. Jameson

The University of Toledo Press

Dedication

We dedicate this book to all the nurses who have lived the joys and the challenges of diploma nursing education.

Acknowledgements

Thank you to Dan, Stacie (whose going back to school to be a nurse planted the seed for this book), and Kimberly. You are my blessings.

– Patricia Ringos Beach MSN, RN, AOCN, ACHPN

I would like to dedicate this book to my aunt, Mary Lou French Yetis RN, who, when I was unsure what career to pursue, suggested that I enter nursing school. She helped me to learn and grow as a nurse. She believed in me throughout her life, and I am ever thankful to her for support and encouragement.

– Susan J. Eisel MSEd, BSN, RN

I dedicate my introductory chaper to all of the current and future nurses that I work with on a daily basis in my role as Nursing Librarian. In addition, I am most grateful to the five authors of this book. Beth, Judy, Maria, Patti, and Sue: thank you for welcoming me with warm hearts into your writing group.

– Jodi S. Jameson, MLIS, AHIP

To Sr. Patricia Ann Dalke, the bravest woman I have had the privilege to know. She knew me as a student and still hired me as a faculty member. She provided me the opportunity to continue to be a part of diploma nursing education and to help make sure that the Mercy heritage lived on through Mercy College of Ohio. To Patti, Beth, Judy, Sue, and Jodi: thank you for the chance to be part of this great adventure with you.

– Maria E. Nowicki, PhD, RN

Thank you to my diploma nursing school for getting me started in this wonderful profession of nursing. Thank you to all of the nursing colleagues with whom I have had the pleasure of working over the years, especially the faculty members of the Toledo Hospital School of Nursing who were so inspirational. And thank you to my co-authors for allowing me to participate in this wonderful project of preserving diploma nursing school history.

– Judy Harris Szor MSN, MEd, RN

I dedicate my contribution to David Nelson White who never stopped believing.

– Beth E. White MSN, RN, CNS

The University of Toledo Press

www.utoledopress.com

Caps, Capes, and Caring:
The Legacy of Diploma Nursing Schools in Toledo

Edited by Barbara Floyd

Book design by Stephanie Delo

Project assistance from Yarko Kuk, Erin Gariepy, and Bryce Bullins.

The photo on the cover is of three nursing students
dressed to go outside. The capes were part of their uniforms.
(Photo courtesy of Mercy College of Ohio archives)

ISBN 978-0-692-10207-7

TABLE OF CONTENTS

Preface

"Were there none who were discontented with what they have, the world would never reach anything better."

– Florence Nightingale

Ecclesiates 3 King James Version:

To everthing there is a season, and a time to every purpose under the heaven:

A time to be born, and a time to die; a time to plant,
and a time to pluck up that which is planted;

A time to kill, and a time to heal; a time to break down,
and a time to build up;

A time to weep, and a time to laugh; a time to mourn,
and a time to dance;

A time to cast away stones, and a time to gather stones together; a time to
embrace and a time to refrain from embracing;

A time to get, and a time to lose; a time to keep, and a time to cast away;

A time to rend, and a time to sew; a time to keep silence,
and a time to speak;

A time to love, and a time to hate; a time of war, and a time of peace.

Nothing stays the same. Through dramatic change and ordinary events, the world evolves. This evolution pertains to all facets of our families, society, and community. It pertains to science and healthcare, to nursing and nursing education.

Between 1893 and 1999, eight hospital based diploma schools of nursing operated in Toledo. Registered nurse graduates from these schools are still among us and continue to provide care and comfort. Just as it seems everyone knows a nurse, in Toledo it is likely that the nurse graduated from one of these schools: Flower Hospital School of Nursing, Maumee Valley Hospital School of Nursing, Mercy Hospital School of Nursing, Riverside Hospital School of Nursing, Robinwood/St. Luke's Hospital School of Nursing, St. Vincent Hospital School of Nursing, Toledo Hospital School of Nursing, and Toledo State Hospital School of Nursing. This core group of schools, operating for just over 100 years, sent registered nurses into our lives to care for our sick and teach us how to stay healthy.

Today, as new collegiate schools to educate nurses have opened, reunions of diploma school nursing classes are common. Some groups meet regularly, others mark special anniversaries. Many friends meet informally as time allows. Some meet at work, because they are still staffing hospitals, clinics, home health agencies, extended care facilities, and other places where care is needed. Bonds of the professional nurse and of lifelong friendships forged during nursing school continue to be cemented. And still, things change.

Recognizing change and understanding that time may obscure and eventually destroy memories and treasures is a strong motivator for documenting history. This was certainly true for us in writing this book.

One of this book's co-authors, a diploma school nurse and mother whose daughter was in a baccalaureate nursing school, closely watched what nursing school was like in the twenty-first century. Besides bringing back memories that were at least 30 years old, her observations evoked familiar feelings; the excitement of observing a first birth, the sadness of death, the large amount of information that had to be learned, the stress of being responsible for another person's life … these do not change much. But, there were striking differences: modern students purchase all required texts in digital versions so that all information is readily available on an electronic device; simulation labs give them experiences that are just shy of the "real" thing; National Council Licensure Examination or NCLEX exams for licensure are now taken on a computer at an individual monitored station in any major city in Ohio.

The mom marveled at and understood these things, but when she told stories of her own education where she practiced injections on fellow students; carried large textbooks; and worked clinicals 24 or more hours per week; the looks she received were sometimes incredulous. Finally, her story that all graduate nurses in the state of Ohio took their licensure exam in Columbus on the same two days, offered twice a year, was almost too much for the daughter. The notion that for two days, every graduate nurse in the state – armed with a pair of number two pencils with erasers – took the licensure exam at the Ohio State Fair Grounds and then waited three months for the results, was a story almost beyond belief. "I can't even imagine that, mom," she said.

Who would remember these things? Who would tell the stories? Five nurses would collaborate on a book about diploma schools in Toledo. Perhaps, as some have suggested, a book with five authors is a book written by a committee. That might be true of some books but not this one. This book was written by five friends, but more importantly nurse colleagues.

We met in the 1980s while faculty members at The Toledo Hospital School of Nursing under the leadership of Margie Place, MSN, RN. With her guidance, the entire faculty worked well together. There was support, camaraderie, and acknowledgement of jobs well done. There was room for everyone and one person's shining moment did not diminish the brightness of another's.

But again nothing stays the same. Faculty members, and even these five nurses, moved on to other jobs. When the school closed in 1988, they all dispersed. Friendships, families, and careers continued. Nursing and nursing education evolved. By 1999 this evolution included the closing of all hospital based diploma schools of nursing in Toledo. An end of an era was noted and tributes were paid to those schools for their contributions to our community.

We began our work as co-authors in 2014. Our book documenting the legacy of diploma schools of nursing in Toledo was meant to contain a fact-based narrative. We started with our own memories. Only one of us had not graduated from a Toledo diploma school of nursing though she came from a diploma school in Youngstown. We had all been educators in diploma schools of nursing in Toledo. These credentials were a strong beginning to bring stories and pictures that would be shared with a wider audience thanks to the University of Toledo Press.

Beyond the facts, what was it like to be a student nurse in school during these wildly different eras? The stories do not stand alone but are ensconced in their times; 1900 was as different from 1950 as 1950 was from 1999. The context of time is important.

The belief in the importance of what a nurse does was also central to writing this book. According to the American Nurses Association's *American Journal of Nursing*, "Nursing is the protection, promotion, and optimization of health and abilities, prevention of illness and injury, facilitation of healing, alleviation of suffering through the diagnosis and treatment of human response, and advocacy in the care of individuals, families, groups, communities, and populations."

Nurses are not "handmaidens" or "doctor 'wanna-bes.'" Nurses are professionals that care for people in their responses to health and disease in a holistic manner. As you read through this 100 or so year history of nursing education in Toledo with glimpses of the bigger national and international pictures, you will witness the change in status as a profession. It is noteworthy that these changes occurred because of nurses, mostly women, pushing for needed healthcare improvements. Nurses courageously helping nursing are part of the context of time.

This context also included a way to think, using the nursing process. Every professional nurse recognizes assessment, diagnosis, planning, implementation, and evaluation as the way to address a patient situation. It is the way to determine what is needed. For example, a nurse might administer chemotherapy to a patient with cancer, but for that a physician's order is needed and followed. It is the physician who prescribes treating the cancer with surgery, chemotherapy and/ or radiation therapy. The nurse treats that patient's responses to the disease and to medical treatment. So as cancer treatment progresses, among other things the nurse will look for signs of pain, nausea, fatigue, weakened immune system and prescribe interventions that will help alleviate these problems and evaluate how well interventional measures work. The family's reaction to illness and treatment and the need for ongoing support will also be assessed and addressed appropriately. This is the art and science of nursing in caring for a patient and family.

One more note to understanding the context of time and nursing, are the different recognized professional nursing education pathways. All registered nurses (RNs) take the same standardized licensure exam, now called standardized National Council Licensure Examination (NCLEX)-RN. To be eligible to take this exam, a candidate must have successfully completed an accredited program of study at either the undergraduate or graduate levels.

Undergraduate programs are a Diploma in Nursing available through hospital-based schools of nursing, an Associate Degree in Nursing (ADN) two-year degree offered by community colleges and some hospital-based schools of nursing, or a Bachelor of Science in Nursing (BS/BSN) four-year degree offered at colleges and universities.

Graduate levels of study are considered advanced practice nurses and include nurse practitioners (NP), clinical nurse specialists (CNS), certified nurse midwives (CNM) and certified registered nurse anesthetists (CRNA). Graduate studies include Master's Degree (MSN) programs designed to prepare Advanced Practice Nurses, nurse administrators, and nurse educators; Doctor of Philosophy (PhD) programs whose graduates typically are prepared to teach and/or conduct research, and Doctor of Nursing Practice (DNP) programs focusing on clinical practice or leadership roles.

A nurse is a nurse is a nurse is not true today, and may have never been true. For this reason the authors had to move from their personal experiences to a wider array of experience to give a better picture of diploma nursing education in Toledo.

As the book evolved, the authors had tremendous help from several librarians and archivists. Special thanks go to Jodi Jameson, Assistant Professor and Nursing Librarian at the University of Toledo, for her knowledge and enthusiasm for this project. Her introduction was an obvious work of love and gives the context of time. In her heart, she knows nursing.

Archivists and librarians who were there to help with any query and added much support to our research were Erin Baker and Lisa Nichols at Mercy St. Vincent Medical Center, Joanna Russ at ProMedica, Elizabeth Tore and Mike Whalen at Mercy College of Ohio, and Sara Mouch at the University of Toledo.

We thank also readers Susan Pitcher and Joanna Russ for your invaluable insights, time, and talents as we prepared to send the manuscript to press. Thank you to Lindsay Gregory, Communications/Recruitment Specialist, University of Toledo who supported and promoted our work even before it was published.

The stories, the stories, the stories. The layers are many; this is only one book. So many nurses took time to talk, interview, share written memoirs, email, and Facebook us to tell us what nursing school was like for them. Every interview left us with a sense of wonder. That is the wonder that the ordinary life remembered and unfolded is remarkable. Thank you to Barbara Halpin Adamczak, Mary Griffiths Andrews, Carol C. Annesser, Joanna Grilli Anthony, Mary Ann Shea Arquette, Mary Depner Beam, Sharon Bee, Anita Boardman Bersticker, Kathy Curley

Bishop, Bonnie Hummel Borgelt, Lissa Wilhelm Brehm, Michelle Beavers Breitfelder, Alice U. Calabrese, Sandy Coldiron Choate, Karen Steinmetz Christian, Janice Smith Cook, Anita Kowaski Cygnor, Victoria Vaughn Dillon, Glenda Drewyor, Jeanne Ann Calabrese Drouillard, Alene Duerk, Elizabeth Ellis-Moore, Pat Yancy Felton, Martha Cook Firstenberger, Sue Foos, Debbie Fritz, Joyce Fry, Mary Ann Graves, Mary Booker Gregory, Ann Richardson Gullberg, Rebecca Rayle Haberkamp, Annette Mazzurco Hallett, Elaine Studer Hetherwick, Sandra Franklin Holloway, Catherine VanVorce Horner, Arlene Albers Hustwick, Cathy Frame Jaworski, Gayle Jeffrey, Diane Knoblauch, Mary Unger Krill, Barbara Rule Krochmalny, Norma Provencher Lake, Lynn Kitchen Langel, Naomi Crow Layman, Betty Spencer Lemon, Sandra Frye Eastep Lohmeyer, Linda Graver Lucas, Jeff Lycan, Loretta Mackey, Sue Maltman, Marilyn Meinen, Alice Miller, Barbara Moellman, Lois Moore, Peggy Galloway Myers, Suzanne Mary Alexander Owen, Sandy Crunkilton Pirwitz, E. Wanda Foltz Quay, Hope J. Wyse Renton, Odette Ann Leininger Rolan, Mary Findlay Root, Luanne Abel Scouten, Linda Shaw, Carol Manley Singer, Amy Smith, Lois Anspach Smith, Luann Schuerman Snyder, Christine Surratt, Nancy R. Swartz, Janette Kish Tangeman, Mary Margraf Tucker, Kathleen Beck VanEtten, Sharon Kitchen Viers, Sheila Wagonlander, Sr. Rita Mary Wasserman, Carolyn Horn Welsh, Virginia Williams Whitmore, Beth Kaltenbach Wilhelm, Kaye Lani Rae Rafko Wilson, Jan Sopher Young, and Cassandra Willey Zak.

The pictures and stories touched our hearts. The trust that was given to us to tell these stories cannot be overstated and we are humbled. Any mistakes and missteps are ours alone to claim and we apologize in advance. As you turn these pages may you have a sense of diploma nursing school and be inspired. May you experience the thrill of helping and healing, of living this life, and of learning. May your understanding continue to evolve. May you enjoy the stories.

Introduction

Jodi S. Jameson, MLIS, AHIP
Assistant Professor and Nursing Librarian
Mulford Health Science Library, The University of Toledo

The Historical Legacy of Hospital-Based Nursing Education in the United States

BEGINNINGS

At 9 a.m., on a late summer day in 1872, Linda Richards entered the New England Hospital for Women and Children in Boston to begin her first day of nurse training.[1] The Civil War had ended seven years before, and the United States was undergoing dramatic change and expansion. Hospitals were growing and the need for well-qualified, trained nurses was more apparent than ever. Just two years prior to her admittance at the New England Hospital, Richards, a former teacher, began pursuing her lifelong dream of caring for the sick by working as a ward maid at Boston City Hospital. However, the duties of housekeeping, cooking, and laundry, for a pay of seven dollars a month, were less than fulfilling and not at all what she expected. So, when Richards read a newspaper advertisement for a formal nurse training program at the New England Hospital, the first of its kind, she could not pass up the opportunity to apply for admission. [2] The training Richards underwent as a student nurse from 1872 to 1873 reads like a type of nursing boot camp:

> Our days were not eight hours; they were nearer twice eight.
> We rose at 5:30 a.m. and left the wards at 9 p.m. to go to our beds,
> which were in little rooms between the wards. Each nurse took
> care of her ward of six patients both day and night; often I did

[1] Linda Richards, "Early Days in the First American Training School for Nurses," *The American Journal of Nursing* 16, no. 3 (1915): 174.

[2] Victoria L. Holder, "From Handmaiden to Right Hand: The Infancy of Nursing," *AORN Journal* 79, no. 2 (2004): 374-390.

not get to sleep before the next call came; but being blessed with a sound body and a firm resolution to go through the training school, cost what it might, I maintained a cheerful spirit.[3]

After graduating in September 1873, with her diploma quietly bestowed on her with no pomp and circumstance, Richards became America's first trained nurse. Her personal account of this legendary status is characteristically humble and modest: "Any distinction which has come to me as the first trained nurse in America arises solely from the fact that I was the first student to enter the new organized school, and so the first to graduate from it."[4] Richards went on to become one of the great pioneers in nursing education, serving as superintendent at several of the most influential nurse training schools in the country including the Boston Training School at Massachusetts General Hospital. Richards's story represents the beginning of a rich legacy of hospital-based nursing education in the United States.

Hospital-Based Nursing Education in Toledo

This book tells the story of nursing pioneers, champions and heroes in Toledo, Ohio, where nursing education has blossomed and thrived since 1893 with the establishment of the Toledo Training School for Nurses. Over the course of a century, eight hospital-based nursing diploma schools existed in Toledo. In 1999, the St. Vincent Hospital School of Nursing was the last of these schools to close. Its closure symbolically marked the end of an era of hospital-based nursing education in Toledo. Yet, the legacy left behind by the eight Toledo diploma schools still lives on today. The following chapters explore this educational legacy by celebrating the conceptual foundations of nursing

[3]Linda Richards, *Reminiscences of Linda Richards: America's First Trained Nurse* (Boston: Whitcomb & Barrows, 1911), 10-11.
[4]Ibid., 12.

education in Toledo as told through stories, photographs, memories, and the words of diploma school graduates and faculty.

Contemporary academic nursing education, which in Toledo and northwest Ohio now includes associate, baccalaureate, master and doctorate programs, owes its foundations to the early hospital-based diploma schools. Today's nursing students and educators live this legacy every day in the classroom and on clinical rotations. The emphasis on clinical education; the curricular focus on patient-centered care; the application of new knowledge, theory, and research to nursing practice; and above all, the unique role of nursing not only as a profession, but as a way of life, a true calling – these are the key components of the legacy which we know today as the art and science of nursing.

This 100-year period in nursing history, from the origins of the first hospital-based diploma schools to their marked decline in the mid to late twentieth century, coincides directly with the professionalization of nursing itself, not to mention numerous social and cultural events including great medical and scientific advances, wars, immigration, economic crises, women's suffrage and liberation, and civil rights. The art and science of nursing did not grow out of a vacuum. To fully understand and appreciate nursing education in the United States today, and in Toledo and northwest Ohio, it is essential to look at the origins, growth, and expansion of hospital-based nursing diploma schools within a historical, social, and cultural context from a national perspective. Though diploma programs for nursing have declined rapidly since the latter part of the twentieth century, without these early schools, nursing education as we know it today would never have been possible.

POST-CIVIL WAR AMERICA AND THE NEED FOR TRAINED NURSES

"We need good, well-trained nurses by the thousand. Every community, throughout the length and breadth of the land, should be supplied with them . . ."[5]

– Samuel D. Gross, MD, from his report entitled "Remarks on the Training of Nurses," presented at the annual meeting of the American Medical Association in May 1869

Dr. Samuel D. Gross and the Call for Nurse Training Schools

Dr. Samuel D. Gross is perhaps most well-known for being the subject of *The Gross Clinic* by American painter Thomas Eakins. Painted in 1875, this masterpiece of American portraiture shows the celebrated surgeon at work in the operating theatre, sparing no detail of the graphic nature of the scene, while also showing an entire absence of aseptic surgical technique not uncommon to the era. Alarming in its realism, the portrait sent shockwaves through the art world when it was exhibited at the 1876 United States Centennial Exposition in Philadelphia.[6] Just seven years before the unveiling of his portrait, Dr. Gross was at the forefront of yet another groundbreaking milestone when he presented a report entitled "Remarks on the Training of Nurses" at the 1869 American Medical Association (AMA) meeting in New Orleans.

Gross, a founding member and two-time president of the AMA, presented his report on nurse training at a time when the nation was in the throes of Reconstruction following the Civil War. During the Civil War, nursing was viewed as a noble, patriotic, and sacrificial

---

[5] Samuel D. Gross, *Remarks on the Training of Nurses* (Philadelphia: Collins, 1869), 5.

[6] Gary E. Friedlaender and Linda K. Friedlaender, "Art in Science: The Gross Clinic by Thomas Eakins," *Clinical Orthopaedics and Related Research* 472, no. 12 (2014): 3632-3636.

calling for women to serve their country by caring for the sick and wounded. However, when the war ended, and women were called back to home and hearthside in their primary roles as wives, mothers, daughters, homemakers, and family caregivers, the societal prejudices toward nursing began to resurface. Late nineteenth-century Victorian social norms of the day dictated that nursing was lowly work suitable for untrained domestics, certainly not an acceptable occupation for nice women from genteel backgrounds. This attitude soon changed. Many of the strong, educated, and intelligent women who had served as nurses during the Civil War, including Clara Barton, Dorothea Dix, and Louisa May Alcott, did much to prove to the public the beneficial effects of good nursing and their examples inspired Gross and others to recommend much-needed nursing reform for the masses. Also, the "Mother of Modern Nursing" Florence Nightingale was making great strides in nursing reform in England, and news of her groundbreaking system of nursing education was starting to garner the attention of physicians like Gross.

The provision of adequate healthcare was an essential component of rebuilding the nation after the Civil War, and Gross recognized that trained nurses were integral to that process: "The subject of nursing possesses a deep national interest"[7] he stated in his now famous address at the 1869 AMA meeting in New Orleans. Gross's address provides great insight into the social ideals of womanhood at the time which thereby influenced the image and role of nurses. For the status of nursing to be elevated to an art and a science, or a "calling" in the eyes of Florence Nightingale, nurses needed to be trained and socialized to exhibit the angelic ideals of nineteenth-century womanhood. In his address, Gross put forth recommended qualifications of the ideal nurse. Her age should be between 22 and 35 at the beginning of her career. She must be of "sound constitution" and possess a "common education"

---

[7]Gross, 4.

with the ability to read and write. She should have a "gentle and refined disposition, courageous, patient, temperate, punctual, cheerful, discreet, honest, sympathizing." Most importantly: "Her moral character should be of the purest kind."[8]

Gross also proposed recommended educational requirements that nurse training schools should offer including principles of hygiene, preparation of food and drink, medication administration, and proper handling of patients suffering from disease or injury.[9] He also provided a detailed history and discussion of successful models of nursing education including the school established by Nightingale in 1860 at the St. Thomas Hospital in London, examples of successful nurse training in Europe by Catholic sisters, and the renowned and highly influential nursing school at Kaiserswerth in Germany where Nightingale was a student before the Crimean War. Gross's argument that Europe and Great Britain had long been ahead of the curve in the education of their nurses, especially in comparison to the embarrassing lack of formalized nurse training in the United States, ignited a spark in the conscience of the medical community. In just under five years following Gross's report, the first formalized hospital-based nursing diploma schools in the United States were founded on the east coast.

A School of Firsts: The New England Hospital for Women and Children

"We pioneer nurses entered the school with a strong desire to learn . . . What we learned we learned thoroughly, and it has proved a good foundation for the building of subsequent years."[10]

– Linda Richards, Reminiscences, 1911

---

[8]Ibid., 14.

[9]Ibid., 15.

[10]Richards, *Reminiscences of Linda Richards: America's First Trained Nurse*, 14.

In 1872, a formal one-year nurse training program was instituted at the New England Hospital for Women and Children in Boston.[11] The nurse training school at the New England Hospital was a school of firsts, for several reasons. It was the first nurse training school in the United States offering formal courses leading to a diploma. It graduated America's first trained nurse Linda Richards on September 1, 1873, and the first African-American trained nurse Mary Eliza Mahoney on August 1, 1879.[12] Progressive in nature, the New England Hospital for Women and Children was a pioneering institution of women's healthcare in America. It was a hospital founded by female physicians for female patients. Also, the training of female medical students and nurses was built into its original purpose and design at the urging of innovative founder Dr. Marie Zakrzewska.[13]

The one-year curriculum at the New England Hospital, modeled after the German method of nurse training at Kaiserswerth, was the idea of 25-year old resident physician Dr. Susan Dimock, who had studied medicine in Germany.[14] The first class at the New England Hospital, consisting of Linda Richards and four other student nurses, was pioneering in spirit. There were no entrance or final examinations. Nursing textbooks were unheard of. Uniforms were not even required yet. The only stipulation was that nurses' chosen dresses "should be washable."[15] In just one year, students underwent training in medical, surgical, and obstetrical nursing. A series of lectures were given by visiting physicians. Student nurses received their practical instruction on the hospital wards from young female physician interns. This system

[11]Althea T. Davis, "America's First School of Nursing: The New England Hospital for Women and Children," *Journal of Nursing Education* 30, no. 4 (1991): 159.

[12]Ibid., 158.

[13]Ibid.

[14]Ibid., 159.

[15]Richards, *Reminiscences of Linda Richards: America's First Trained Nurse*, 11.

of "learning by doing" at the patient's bedside was characteristic of the early training schools. As Linda Richards stated, "We were supposed to understand and act."[16] Also characteristic of the early days of nurse training were the long hours and the demanding schedules endured by students. There was little, if any, time for recreation or leisure. In her year at the New England Hospital, Richards recalled being off duty every second week for just one afternoon, between 2 p.m. and 5 p.m. She was granted leave only twice to attend church.[17]

While highly demanding, the training school at the New England Hospital made great advances in improving the image of nursing. This was a crucial step toward legitimizing nursing education. At the New England Hospital, the education of nurses was of equal importance as the education of physicians. Characterized by forward-thinking feminist ideals, the New England Hospital would set the foundations for formalized nurse training in the United States, including the groundbreaking Nightingale-modeled schools at Bellevue, New Haven, and Massachusetts General, all founded in 1873.

NURSING EDUCATION IN THE AGE OF REFORM

"… I saw at once that no permanent improvement in the condition of the Hospital could be made until the nursing service was radically changed and that this could only be accomplished through the establishment of a training school for nurses."[18]

– Louisa Lee Schuyler recalling her 1871 visit to Bellevue Hospital in New York City

The Gilded Age in America has also been called the "age of

---

[16] Ibid., 12.

[17] Ibid., 11.

[18] Dorothy Giles, *A Candle in Her Hand: A Story of the Nursing Schools of Bellevue Hospital* (New York: G.P. Putnam's Sons, 1949), 67.

reform."[19] During this period, much attention was drawn to the problematic state of social institutions including hospitals which were growing in vast numbers. Out of this need for hospital reform came the establishment of nurse training schools with the aim of improving hospital conditions and increasing patient safety. In 1873, the famous trio of nurse training schools opened on the east coast: Bellevue, New Haven, and Massachusetts General. While the New England Hospital for Women and Children was the first of its kind in the United States to provide formalized hospital-based nursing education leading to a diploma, these three schools in 1873 were the first to be modeled after the system of nurse training established by Florence Nightingale in England. The founding of these schools was influenced by committees made up of prominent philanthropic society women with a common interest in charitable measures and social reform.[20] One of these women was Louisa Lee Schuyler, who led the formation of the first Nightingale school in the United States, the Training School for Nurses at Bellevue Hospital in New York City.

1873: The Year of the Nightingale Schools

Louisa Lee Schuyler was the great-granddaughter of Alexander Hamilton.[21] Although she was brought up in privileged surroundings, she was no stranger to hard work. She had a sharp intellect, boundless energy, and a zeal for social reform having been a member of the United States Sanitary Commission during the Civil War.[22] Her work with the Sanitary Commission taught her the art of organizing groups of likeminded individuals for the common good, most notably the

[19]Richard Hofstadter, *The Age of Reform: From Bryan to F.D.R.* (New York: Vintage Books, 1955).

[20]Josephine Dolan, "Nurses in American History: Three Schools: 1873," *The American Journal of Nursing* 75, no. 6 (1975).

[21]Giles, 57-58.

[22] Ibid., 61-63.

improvement of Civil War hospital conditions and the care of soldiers. On the afternoon of January 26, 1872, Schuyler organized a group of well-educated, cultured women in the drawing room of her family home at 19 East 31st Street in Manhattan to discuss the current state of hospitals in New York City, most notably Bellevue.[23] This group eventually formed a Visiting Committee whose principle charge was to inspect Bellevue Hospital to "inform themselves and others about conditions there, and with the ultimate aim of bringing about improvements where possible."[24] One of these improvements would be the establishment of a nurse training school.

Elizabeth Hobson, one member of the Visiting Committee, had never once set foot in a hospital before. On her visit to Bellevue, she nearly fainted by what she saw and had to return another day after her strength and courage had improved.[25] Her description of Bellevue is quite typical of large city hospitals at the time:

> The condition of the patients and the beds was unspeakable; the one nurse slept in the bath-room, and the tub was filled with filthy rubbish. As for the nurse, she was an Irish woman of a low class, and to her was confided the care of twenty patients, her only assistants being paupers, so-called 'helpers,' women drafted from the workhouse, many of whom had been sent there for intemperance, and those convalescents who could leave their beds.[26]

This troubling image of a nurse sleeping in a bathroom, with "paupers" and convalescent patients serving as her assistants, not to mention the 20 poor souls left to their care, was exactly what the

---

[23] Ibid., 67.

[24] Ibid., 68.

[25] Elizabeth Hobson, *Recollections of a Happy Life* (New York: G.P. Putnam's Sons, 1916), 81.

[26] Ibid., 82.

Nightingale-modeled nurse training schools of 1873 so desperately desired to remedy. Yet another problem in hospitals was the serious lack of infection control. Hobson was witness to this at Bellevue where physicians used the same sponge "on one patient after another without any disinfection."[27] Louis Pasteur's germ theory and Joseph Lister's principles of aseptic surgical technique were not yet widely accepted by society and were only beginning to influence medical practice in some American hospitals.[28] The attention drawn to hospitals during this age of reform, and the influence of women's committees such as that at Bellevue, not only helped to establish nurse training schools but also brought to the public's attention the need for wide acceptance of infection control. In turn, trained nurses would play a major role in patient safety and in controlling infection rates in hospitals throughout the next century.

On May 1, 1873, after sufficient funds were raised and consent obtained from the Commissioners of Charities and the Bellevue Medical Board, the new nurse training school at Bellevue Hospital opened with its first class of six pupils.[29] The work of the women's Visiting Committee led by Louisa Lee Schuyler had been successful in establishing the first Nightingale-modeled nurse training school in the United States. Similar schools opened in immediate succession. On October 6, 1873, the Connecticut Training School for Nurses at the New Haven Hospital opened with a class of four pupils.[30] The Boston Training School at Massachusetts General Hospital opened one month later on November 1, 1873.[31] These three schools were instrumental in the development

---

[27] Ibid., 86.

[28] Ellen Davidson Baer, "Key Ideas in Nursing's First Century," *The American Journal of Nursing* 112, no. 5 (2012): 50.

[29] Giles, 96.

[30] Margaret K. Stack, "Resume of the History of the Connecticut Training School for Nurses," *The American Journal of Nursing* 23, no. 10 (1923): 826.

[31] Mrs. Curtis and Miss Denny, "Early History of the Boston Training-School," ibid.2, no. 5 (1902): 334.

of hospital-based nursing education in the United States. Bellevue in particular grew in size and influence over the years. The student nurses at Bellevue have become the stuff of legend in nursing history symbolism with their blue and white seersucker uniforms and Tiffany & Company-designed nursing pins. Bellevue began to set the standard for nurse training in these early days. In 1878, Bellevue published its own *Manual of Nursing* for use at the school. The Bellevue *Manual* provides keen insight into typical nurse training of the day, in addition to numerous societal norms, beliefs and attitudes that characterized the Nightingale model of hospital-based nursing education in late nineteeth century America.[32]

Excerpts from *A Manual of Nursing Prepared for the Training School for Nurses Attached to Bellevue Hospital* (1878):

- "Let it be remembered that the care which the nurse gives her patient will often decide the question of life or death, and her calling will then assume the dignity which really belongs to it" (p. 3).
- "The best age to begin the study of nursing is from 25 to 35 years; it would be a very exceptional case in which it could be successfully commenced after the age of 35" (p. 3).
- "High-heeled boots are out of place in the sick-room" (p. 4).
- "Patients are generally ready to converse more freely with the nurse than with the physician" (p. 23).
- "Sometimes when they [leeches] persist in refusing to bite, if they are put into a plate with some beer, and then held firmly by the tail they will fix themselves almost immediately" (p. 52).

---

[32]*A Manual of Nursing Prepared for the Training School for Nurses Attached to Bellevue Hospital*, (New York: G.P. Putnam's Sons, 1878), https://archive.org/details/101509349.nlm.nih.gov.

- "If ether is to be administered, the patient should have a pint of beef-tea four hours before the operation, and should have nothing else, except perhaps a little brandy" (p. 68).
- "Remember never to be a gossip or tattler" (p. 141).
- "Never contradict your patient, nor argue with him, nor let him see that you are annoyed about anything" (p. 141).

With the establishment of these Nightingale-modeled schools, nursing became a respectable and noble educational pursuit for middle class women. To society at the time, nursing was a natural extension of women's intrinsic domestic and caregiving abilities. The type of training that student nurses received in the infancy of hospital-based education has been described as a "modified apprenticeship" style.[33] The "learning by doing" model described by Linda Richards still prevailed, and classroom lectures were conducted by physicians. In keeping with the subtle spiritual overtones of Nightingale's influence, student nurses lived in convent-like nurses' homes attached to the hospitals where they received their training. This architectural symbolism of student nurses being attached to the hospital was intentional in ensuring that students were acculturated and socialized into the life of the hospital.[34] Students did not pay tuition. In return for their work on the wards, they were paid a small allowance by the hospital while receiving room and board. Over time, this system inevitably led to abuses. Student nurses were often exploited as a form of cheap labor to meet the increasing demands at hospitals for a nursing workforce.[35] As historian Susan Reverby insightfully states: "Nursing education was called training; in reality it was work."[36]

---

[33] Jane E. Murdock, "Evolution of the Nursing Curriculum," *Journal of Nursing History* 2, no. 1 (1986): 18.

[34] Susan Gelfand Malka, *Daring to Care: American Nursing and Second-Wave Feminism* (Urbana, Illinois: University of Illinois Press, 2007), 39.

[35] Susan M. Reverby, *Ordered to Care: The Dilemma of American Nursing, 1850-1945* (Cambridge, UK: Cambridge University Press, 1987), 62.

[36] Ibid., 60.

By the turn of the twentieth century, there were 432 hospital-based nursing schools in the United States.[37] The rise of the modern hospital in the late nineteenth century created and nurtured the early nurse training schools. Also around this time, a slow but gradual shift away from the apprenticeship model began to take place. Notable graduates of the early diploma schools began to recognize that nursing was not simply a form of hospital labor, but a genuine profession deserving of its own educational standards and professional organizations. Reformers such as Isabel Hampton, Lavinia Dock, and Mary Adelaide Nutting, all diploma school graduates and close friends, would become the first great nursing education leaders in the United States. Their lasting contributions would set the stage for ushering in a modern approach to nursing education.

THE NEW NURSE AT THE TURN OF THE CENTURY

"I am single, and my life is my own, to do as I please with, from now on."[38]

– Mary Heriot in her application letter
to the Johns Hopkins Training School for Nurses

This quote by a prospective student nurse encapsulates a certain independence of spirit that must have been felt by so many young women who chose to enter nursing in the late nineteenth century. This was the era of women's suffrage and the ideals of early feminism were in the air. Still, few career options were open to women at the time. Nurse training schools offered a path for unmarried women to enter an

---

[37]Teresa E. Christy, "Nurses in American History. The Fateful Decade, 1890-1900," *The American Journal of Nursing* 75, no. 7 (1975): 1163-1165.

[38]Janet Wilson James, "Isabel Hampton and the Professionalization of Nursing in the 1890s," in *The Therapeutic Revolution: Essays in the Social History of American Medicine*, ed. Morris J. Vogel and Charles E. Rosenberg (University of Pennsylvania Press, 1979): 215.

occupation outside of the home and into the world.[39]

The period from 1890 to 1900 has been termed "the fateful decade" by nursing historian Teresa E. Christy.[40] It was a time of educational reform that led to the legitimization of nursing as a profession. It was also a time of development and growth in the United States characterized by industrialization, urbanization, and immigration, which in turn led to an increase in the number of hospitals. In 1873, when the first Nightingale-modeled schools were founded on the east coast, 178 hospitals existed in the United States. By 1909, this number had reached 4,359.[41] To meet the demand for nurses to provide patient care at hospitals, the number of nurse training schools increased rapidly, but the quality of training decreased. In turn-of-the-century America, there was no more influential advocate for quality improvement in nursing education than Isabel Hampton.

Isabel Hampton: Nursing Education Innovator

In 1882, while Isabel Hampton was a student nurse at Bellevue, *The Century Magazine* published a richly detailed account of the famous Nightingale-modeled school. Written by Franklin H. North, the article was fittingly entitled "A New Profession for Women."[42] It provided the public with an insightful portrayal of nurse training in the early years of diploma schools, including details and experiences of which Hampton would have undoubtedly been familiar.[43] Contained within the article's pages is a sketch of a Bellevue nurse, depicting a focused young woman

[39]Ibid., 214.

[40]Christy, 493.

[41]Charles E. Rosenberg, *The Care of Strangers: The Rise of America's Hospital System* (New York: Basic Books, 1987), 5.

[42]Franklin H. North, "A New Profession for Women," *The Century Magazine* (November 1882): 38-47.

[43]Ethel Johns and Blanche Pfefferkorn, "Isabel Hampton," in *The Johns Hopkins Hospital School of Nursing: 1889-1949* (Baltimore: The Johns Hopkins Press, 1954), 41.

carefully and meticulously measuring out medicine to be administered to a patient. This portrait captures the essence of nurses like Hampton who epitomized professionalism, attention to detail, and commitment to excellence. Hampton's embodiment of these characteristics would become instrumental in setting high standards for nursing education in the late nineteeth through early twentieth centuries.

Born in 1859 in the small town of Welland, Ontario, Hampton worked as a teacher in Canada before deciding to become a nurse. She enrolled at Bellevue in 1881, a member of one of the earliest classes at the legendary school. After graduating in 1883, Hampton worked in Rome at St. Paul's House for Trained Nurses for eighteen months, an experience that undoubtedly shaped and broadened her worldview of nursing. In 1886, she returned to the United States where she obtained the position of superintendent at the Illinois Training School for Nurses at the Cook County Hospital in Chicago. It was here that Hampton began to demonstrate her remarkable organizational abilities and forward-thinking leadership. Her greatest accomplishment and legacy was the establishment of the first graded curriculum of nursing. Prior to this, student nurses were not required to demonstrate documented evidence of nursing knowledge to earn a diploma. Hampton's graded curriculum model became the norm at other training schools. It added an element of academic rigor to hospital-based nursing education, while also ensuring greater competency among new nurse graduates. During her tenure of just three years as superintendent at the Illinois Training School, Hampton built a solid reputation for herself grounded in professionalism, accountability, and ethics. In 1889, her reputation for nursing excellence led her to the newly founded Johns Hopkins Hospital in Baltimore where she served as Superintendent of the Training School for Nurses from 1889 to 1894.[44]

[44]Selma Moody, "Isabel Hampton Robb: Her Contribution to Nursing Education," *The American Journal of Nursing* 38, no. 10 (1938): 1131; James, 201-204.

The Hopkins Model and the Influence of Hampton and Nutting

Because of Hampton's groundbreaking efforts, Johns Hopkins became the model against which all future nurse training schools would be judged. Hampton brought to Hopkins the innovations in nurse training that made her respected at the Illinois Training School, including the implementation of a graded course of study. Hampton also proposed that the training program be extended from two years to three years. The longer three-year curriculum, which would be incorporated in 1896 under the leadership of Hampton's successor allowed for the incorporation of theoretical instruction. As Hampton stated during a speech at Hopkins in 1889: "…technical skill can only be acquired through a systematic course of practical and theoretical study under competent teachers."[45] The three-year course of study eventually became the standard duration of all nurse training schools across the country well into the late twentieth century.

This balance of practical and theoretical training, and the emphasis on quality over quantity, was at the heart of Hampton's educational philosophy. This philosophy is strongly reflected in Hampton's 1893 textbook *Nursing: Its Principles and Practice*. The first truly modern nursing textbook, Hampton's book is significant for its detailed content on bacteriology, germ theory, chemistry, pathology and physiology. It also emphasizes nursing as a holistic profession in which the care of the whole person is taken into highest consideration. At the heart of any profession is an application of ethics. Therefore, to further advance nursing as a profession, in 1900 Hampton published the first nursing text on ethics, entitled *Nursing Ethics: For Hospital and Private Use.* She also encouraged the organization of a journal club for nursing students at Hopkins, which promoted the reading, study, and application of

---

[45]Isabel Hampton Robb, *Educational Standards for Nurses with Other Addresses on Nursing Subjects* (Cleveland: E. C. Koeckert, 1907), 34.

articles from American and British medical journals.[46] It may be said that Hampton was an early pioneer of evidence-based nursing practice.

Hampton's influence extended beyond her role as superintendent at Hopkins. In nursing education history, one of the most significant events was the Chicago World's Fair in 1893. It was here that a meeting was held of the International Congress of Charities, Correction and Philanthropy. The greatest nursing minds of the day, including Hampton, presented papers on the status of nursing education. In a significant step toward professionalization and standardization in nursing, the American Society of Superintendents of Training Schools for Nurses was formed by Hampton at the meeting, a precursor to the National League for Nursing.[47] Hampton resigned from Johns Hopkins in 1894 upon her marriage to physician Dr. Hunter S. Robb. They were married in London, with Hampton fittingly carrying a bouquet of flowers from Florence Nightingale. Mary Adelaide Nutting, a graduate of the first class at Hopkins, served as superintendent at the training school following Hampton's departure.

Nutting continued the example of strong leadership set by Hampton and exceeded it exponentially. Along with her success in lengthening the training program to three years, Nutting was also instrumental in eliminating student stipends – a goal strongly advocated for by Hampton. The elimination of stipends ensured that the training school attracted high caliber students who were serious about becoming nurses, rather than those solely motivated by pay. This money was instead more effectively utilized to purchase textbooks and to compensate well-qualified instructors. Nutting also had a passion for reading, research, and critical thinking. Under Nutting's leadership at Hopkins, the nursing library for students was greatly expanded. In 1896, she conducted what

[46]*Our Shared Legacy : Nursing Education at Johns Hopkins, 1889-2006*, ed. Mame Warren (Baltimore: The Johns Hopkins University Press, 2006), 10.

[47]Murdock, 17-18.

is now considered to be one of the first examples of nursing research, a national survey of students' work schedules at nurse training schools. Nutting would eventually go on to become an innovator in collegiate nursing education at the Columbia University Teachers College, where she became the first nurse ever appointed as a university professor.[48] She remained a lifelong friend and colleague of Hampton.

Sadly, Hampton would not live long enough to see the lasting impact of her own influence, as well as that of her colleague Nutting. She was tragically killed by a trolley on Euclid Avenue in Cleveland at the age of 50, leaving behind her husband and two sons.[49] Both Hampton and Nutting set forth modern educational ideals that would have far-reaching impact, not only for hospital-based diploma schools, but for baccalaureate nursing education in the mid-twentieth century.

THE PROFESSIONALIZATION OF NURSING IN THE DAWN OF EARLY FEMINISM

"The task of organizing human happiness needs the active cooperation of man and woman: it cannot be relegated to one half of the world."[50]
– Lillian Wald, founder of public health nursing at the Henry Street Settlement, excerpt from a speech on women's suffrage, 1914

Women's suffrage, early feminism, and the idea of the New Woman would create refashioned roles for women in the early twentieth century. Nurses and suffragettes Lillian Wald and Lavinia Dock were at the forefront of incorporating early feminist ideals into nursing. The image of what it meant to be a nurse was transformed into that of a social reformer for public health advocacy. Public health nursing drastically

[48]Helen E. Marshall, *Mary Adelaide Nutting: Pioneer of Modern Nursing* (Baltimore: The Johns Hopkins University Press, 1972); Stella Goostray, "Mary Adelaide Nutting," *The American Journal of Nursing* 58, no. 11 (1958).

[49]"Editorial Comment: In Memoriam - Isabel Hampton Robb," ibid.10, no. 8 (1910): 29.

[50]*Lillian D. Wald: Progressive Activist*, ed. Claire Coss (New York: The Feminist Press), 83.

changed diploma nursing education and created new professional roles for nurses.

The Origins of Public Health Nursing

In 1895, diploma school graduate Lillian Wald laid the groundwork for social reform in nursing with the founding of the Henry Street Settlement on the Lower East Side of Manhattan. Wald developed the concept of public health nursing, which at the turn of the century was a crucial role to fill to meet the healthcare needs of a growing immigrant population. Lavinia Dock, a graduate of the Bellevue Training School, worked with Wald at Henry Street in providing nursing care, social services, and education to the poor and underserved Lower East Side community. Both women also joined forces in the woman's suffrage movement. Settlement houses, such as that at Henry Street, became havens of progressive social reform among groups of women. They nurtured feminist friendships and promoted public health.[51]

"It was at Henry Street that I really learned to think," reflected Lavinia Dock.[52] Dock lived and worked at the Henry Street Settlement for 20 years. The experiences Dock gained while caring for the poor dramatically shaped her view of nursing. She would go on to become one of the most prolific writers in nursing. The knowledge she gained while at Henry Street, and her passion for the critical role of nurses in promoting the health and well-being of society, culminated in the writing of a four volume *History of Nursing*, co-authored with Mary Adelaide Nutting (1907-12); a nurses' manual on venereal disease entitled *Hygiene and Morality* (1910); and a *History of American Red*

---

[51]Susan M. Poslusny, "Feminist Friendship: Isabel Hampton Robb, Lavinia Lloyd Dock and Mary Adelaide Nutting," *Image: Journal of Nursing Scholarship* 21, no. 2 (1989).

[52]Mary Lou Schwartz, "Lavinia Dock: Adams County Suffragette " *Adams County History* 3 (1997): 73.

Cross Nursing (1922). These books, along with Clara Weeks Shaw's *A Textbook for Nursing* (1885) and Hampton's *Nursing: Its Principles and Practice* (1893), were standard texts in all hospital-based diploma schools.

With its roots in early feminism and social reform, public health nursing created a professional identity for nurses in a changing society. This role would be essential to the nation in the ensuing years of World War I and II. Public health nursing and the care of vulnerable populations soon became a critical aspect of student nurses' training at diploma schools, and it remains an essential component of nursing curricula today.

The American Journal of Nursing

From the early twentieth century to the beginning of World War I, much conversation and discourse surrounded the topic of nursing as a profession, most notably in articles published in *The American Journal of Nursing*. Founded in 1900 by Mary E.P. Davis and Sophia Palmer, with financial support from Isabel Hampton Robb, Mary Adelaide Nutting, and Lavinia Dock, *The American Journal of Nursing* became the first nursing journal in the United States that was completely managed by nurses. It provided a platform for communication of relevant issues facing nursing.[53] In an article published in 1904, nurse Nellie Schwartz presented a passionate argument for nursing as a profession, grounded in early feminist ideals. She argued that nurses alone are responsible for the advancement of their profession:

We, as women, must work out our own salvation . . . It was woman alone who awoke from her mental lethargy to the fact that she is her brother's equal, and once having had the scales fall from her eyes, she made rapid progress and at present stands on the same footing as her brother in the professional field. So with nursing. No one is going to

[53]Philip A. Kalisch and Beatrice J. Kalisch, The Advance of American Nursing (Philadelphia: Lippincott, 1995), 116.

tell us we should be professionalized; we must put this before the public ourselves.[54]

The American Journal of Nursing, along with books by Dock, Nutting, and Hampton, could be found on the shelves of every nursing school library and is a core title in all health science libraries today. The establishment of The American Journal of Nursing, fondly referred to by nurses and nursing students as "The Journal," gave nursing a professional voice for the sharing of ideas and the publication of articles on nursing issues including education.

WORLD WAR I AND ITS AFTERMATH: A CRITICAL TIME FOR NURSING EDUCATION

"And then came the War and all history, social and political, paused for the season of the Great Conflict . . . Disorganization and disruption involved, with everything else, the profession of nursing. Thousands of nurses were lost, for the time being, to America."[55]

– Richard Olding Beard, MD, 2nd Annual Meeting of the Central Council of Nursing Education, Chicago, 1922

In 1912, the Education Committee of the Society for Superintendents had renamed itself the National League of Nursing Education. In 1914, on the eve of World War I, the League began preparing a standard curriculum to be used by nursing schools across the country. The committee preparing the report was led by Mary Adelaide Nutting. Released in 1917, the Standard Curriculum for Schools of Nursing established guidelines for school facilities, student life, and teaching methods, as well as a complete curriculum plan with objectives

---

[54]Nellie Schwartz, "Nursing as a Profession," *The American Journal of Nursing* 4, no. 11 (1904): 835.

[55]Richard Olding Beard, "The Making of History in Nursing Education," ibid.22, no. 7 (1922): 508.

and methods. However, not long after its publication, the Standard Curriculum would need to be revised, largely due to the effects of World War I.

The Nursing Shortage of 1918

In 1918, a severe nursing shortage occurred in the United States due to the deployment of nurses at home and abroad during World War I. Combined with the ruthless influenza epidemic of 1918, the country faced an increased demand for trained nurses, especially public health nurses, to meet the healthcare needs of the population. The experience of the Great War and the influenza epidemic placed nursing under a microscope and revealed several deficiencies in nursing education.[56] During the influenza epidemic, student nurses provided round the clock care to hospital patients, and many became ill as a result – sometimes resulting in death. Dorothy Deming was a student nurse at New York's Presbyterian Hospital in 1918: "The shortage of nurses, already acute because of the demands of war (our hospital alone had more than 50 graduates overseas), was intensified by illness among the staff – 90 of our graduate nurses and students came down with the flu, one died."[57] To remedy existing deficiencies in nursing education, a significant study would be conducted in 1919 that changed nursing education forever.

The Progressive Era and the Goldmark Report

The year 1919 was one of change and empowerment for women. With the passage of the 19th Amendment, women across the nation obtained the right to vote. Also in 1919, an advocate for the work of women, Progressive reformer Josephine Goldmark, began research for the Rockefeller Foundation on the state of nursing education in the

---

[56]Murdock, 18-20.

[57]Dorothy Deming, "Influenza: 1918," *The American Journal of Nursing* 57, no. 10 (1957): 1308.

United States. The Committee for the Study of Nursing Education, led by Goldmark, initially set out to conduct a national study on public health nursing education. However, after much discussion, it was decided to broaden the scope to nursing education in general, including hospital-based training schools. The committee also featured several noteworthy nursing leaders, including Mary Adelaide Nutting and Lillian Wald, as well as educator and founder of the Army School of Nursing Annie Goodrich.

This was not the first time that Goldmark had conducted research on areas of social and labor interest. In 1912 she had published a highly influential report on the relationship between fatigue and long working hours of laborers entitled *Fatigue and Efficiency.* Her extensive research on nursing education for the Rockefeller Foundation would come to be known as the *Goldmark Report.* Goldmark began carrying out her survey research in October 1919. A small group of schools, similar in character, were selected for the study, resulting in a sample of 23 nurse training schools. The report was published in 1923, after four years of in-depth research. One of the main recommendations of the *Goldmark Report* was for nursing education to move out of the hospital and into the university. The *Goldmark Report* also called attention to the poor state of education in some hospital-based schools, which at the time did not require applicants to be high school graduates.[58] Goldmark also strongly advocated for a rigorous academic curriculum in diploma schools, including training in the basic sciences, theoretical instruction, and nutrition. The recommendations from the *Goldmark Report* strongly influenced the revisions made to the original 1917 *Standard Curriculum.* This revision would be published in 1927 under the title *A*

[58]Committee for the Study of Nursing Education, *Nursing and Nursing Education in the United States / Report of the Committee for the Study of Nursing Education ... And Report of a Survey by Josephine Goldmark, Secretary,* ed. Josephine Goldmark (New York: The Macmillan Company, 1923), 220.

Curriculum Guide for Schools of Nursing, which would again be revised in 1937.

THE IMPACT OF THE GREAT DEPRESSION ON NURSING EDUCATION

"In this year 1932 we have been going through one of the worst depressions in our history. It has been combined with the worst unemployment which the nursing profession has ever known."[59]
— *Mary Ayres Burgess, PhD, American Hospital Association*
Meeting, Detroit, September 15, 1932

The stock market crash of 1929, and the ensuing Great Depression, had a major impact on nursing in the United States. Several nursing schools were forced to close due to financial hardship. Also, nursing was not immune to the tide of unemployment that swept the entire nation. Unemployment for nurses in all healthcare settings was at an all-time high. Private duty nurses were put out of work since their patients could no longer afford healthcare. Unemployed nurses in hospital, industrial, and office settings began to seek work in private duty, but there was no work to be found. Also, the nursing applicant pool was increasingly competitive. Married nurses who had previously retired were now seeking employment to contribute to the family income.[60]

However, as history demonstrates, it is not uncommon for great crises to lead to positive changes. In an address to the American Hospital Association in 1932, educator and statistician Mary Ayres Burgess stated: "Not all the results of the depression and of unemployment have been bad."[61] The cataclysmic and detrimental effects of the economic

---

[59]Mary Ayres Burgess, "Quality Nursing," *The American Journal of Nursing* 32, no. 10 (1932): 1050.

[60]Margaret Ashmun, "The Cause and Cure of Unemployment in the Nursing Profession," ibid.33, no. 7 (1933): 652-53.

[61]Burgess, 1050.

depression forced the nursing community to look inward for a solution to unemployment and the problems facing nursing education. The Depression was the catalyst that was needed for many marginal nursing schools to finally close their doors. Yet, the schools that were still open were graduating more nurses than there were available jobs. The nursing workforce had reached a saturation point. Therefore, nursing schools were forced to be more strict and selective than usual with their admission requirements.

In 1934, following the Great Depression, the Committee on the Grading of Schools of Nursing published their report *Nursing Schools: Today and Tomorrow.* Led by Mary Ayres Burgess, the Committee discovered that some hospital-based nursing schools were functioning poorly. As a resulting influence of this report, higher standards for nursing schools were sought. With these improved standards, many higher caliber nursing students were graduating and becoming nursing instructors, thereby resulting in improved instruction at nursing schools. Educational quality at diploma programs would further improve during World War II with the advent of the United States Cadet Nurse Corps.

A CALL TO ACTION: NURSING EDUCATION DURING AND AFTER WORLD WAR II

"We have lost many graduate nurses since December to the Army and the Navy, to first aid stations, and through evacuation. This shortage has increased student responsibilities and left vacancies . . . We all gained much in experience and maturity during the trying days of December 1941 . . ."[62]

> *— Frances Carr, senior nursing student at The Queen's Hospital School of Nursing in Honolulu, reflecting on her experiences during and after the attack on Pearl Harbor*

[62]Frances Carr, "Student Nurse in the War Zone," *The American Journal of Nursing* 42, no. 9 (1942): 1067.

In 1941, on the eve of the United States' entry into World War II, Americans collectively felt a sense of foreboding. The effects of the Depression were still being felt, both economically and psychologically. The war, which was raging in Europe and Great Britain, felt so far away yet seemed so near. On December 7, 1941, everything changed when the Japanese bombed Pearl Harbor. Just four days later, on December 11, President Franklin Delano Roosevelt and Congress announced a declaration of war officially catapulting the United States into World War II. An overwhelming sense of patriotism swept the nation. Many felt called to serve, including nurses. The government strongly appealed for nurses to volunteer in the Army Nurse Corps, and many did, leading to a nursing shortage which would be alleviated by student nurses serving in the United States Cadet Nurse Corps.[63]

The U.S. Cadet Nurse Corps

Hospital-based nursing diploma schools played an integral role in responding to the nursing shortage during World War II. On July 1, 1943, the U.S. Cadet Nurse Corps was established as a result of the Bolton Act sponsored by Ohio Congresswoman Frances Payne Bolton. A direct response to the nursing shortage, the Bolton Act was the first form of federal aid for education in the United States. Some 1,125 hospital-based nursing schools across the country participated in the Cadet Nurse Corps. Students admitted to the Corps had all of their educational expenses paid for including tuition, fees, books, and uniforms, and they also received a stipend, all paid for by the United States Public Health Service. The Cadet Nurse Corps was an attractive opportunity for many struggling families in the post-Depression era who wished to educate their daughters for entry into the respectable profession of nursing. A massive publicity campaign was launched to recruit young women into

---

[63]Marie Breakiron, "A Salute to the Nurses of World War II," *AORN Journal* 62, no. 5 (1995): 710-722.

the Corps. Hugely successful, from 1943 to 1945 the Corps accounted for 83 percent of all student admissions at diploma nursing schools.[64]

The Cadet Nurse Corps had an overall positive effect on the quality of nursing education in mid-twentieth century America. It ultimately helped nursing diploma schools escape the final remnants of the old apprenticeship model of nurse training.[65] The Division of Nurse Education (DNE) placed many restrictions on schools in the program. If schools did not meet standards set by the DNE, then they would not qualify for funds. Students who enrolled in the Cadet Nurse Corps also held the elevated position of serving their country during wartime. This sense of patriotism helped elevate the status of hospital-based nursing education, and therefore of nurses. Importantly, schools that were part of the Cadet Nurse Corps program were required to have a separate budget from the hospital. As such, hospitals were forced to truly consider the nurse training school as a separate entity for the first time. After World War II, this consideration would be taken even further with the publication of one of the most significant works in modern nursing history, Esther Lucile Brown's *Nursing for the Future.*

The Brown Report of 1948

Esther Lucile Brown was not a nurse, but rather a social anthropologist. In 1930, she was hired by the Russell Sage Foundation in New York to conduct comparative research on various professions. Following the World War II nursing shortage, Brown was asked to reevaluate the profession of nursing. Her expertise on the "anthropology of the professions" brought a unique perspective to nursing education.[66]

---

[64]Beatrice J. Kalisch and Philip A. Kalisch, "Nurses in American History. The Cadet Nurse Corps in World War II," *The American Journal of Nursing* 76, no. 2 (1976): 240-242.

[65]Bonnie Bullough, "Nurses in American History. The Lasting Impact of World War II on Nursing," ibid., no. 1 (1976): 118-120.

[66]Juliene G. Lipson, "Esther Lucile Brown - a Memorial," *Image: the Journal of Nursing Scholarship* 24, no. 4 (1992): 314.

Sponsored by the National Nursing Council, Brown's in-depth study took 16 months to complete. It included extensive research on the current state of nursing education, and was based on visits to more than 50 nursing schools and meetings with groups of educators. Like Josephine Goldmark's report on nursing education in 1923, which sought to remedy the deficits in nursing education after World War I, Brown's report of 1948 was a byproduct of the problems and issues facing nursing education in another post-war climate.

In 1965, *The American Journal of Nursing* stated that Brown's report of 1948 "rent nursing asunder."[67] Published with the fitting title *Nursing for the Future*, Brown's study found that not all hospital-based nursing schools were adequately preparing students for entry into nursing. She called these schools "socially undesirable." In 1948, there were approximately 1,250 nursing schools in the United States, and only 6 percent were in higher education.[68] All others were hospital-based diploma programs. Brown's main recommendation, like the *Goldmark Report* of 1923, was that nursing schools should separate themselves from hospitals and move into the college or university setting. The period in nursing education following the publication of Brown's report, marks the beginning of a gradual decline in hospital-based nursing schools.

While Brown's work is mostly cited for its influence on moving nursing education into the university and out of the hospital, her overall body of work, which includes several articles and books on nursing, had a lasting influence on other significant aspects of nursing education. Brown was ahead of her time in many ways. She was an early proponent of the inclusion of cultural competency in nursing practice. As early as the 1930s, she was urging nurses to consider patients' cultural backgrounds when providing nursing care. In *Nursing for the Future*,

---

[67]Esther L. Brown, "Preparation for Nursing," *The American Journal of Nursing* 65, no. 9 (1965).

[68]Esther L. Brown, *Nursing for the Future: A Report Prepared for the National Nursing Council* (New York: Russell Sage Foundation, 1948).

she advocated for men and minorities to enter the nursing profession
and for hospital-based nursing schools to welcome them. Throughout
her long career, Brown was embraced by the nursing community for
her contributions, and was declared a lifelong honorary member of the
National League for Nursing. Brown's research is one of the greatest
legacies of the hospital-based era of nursing education. It would be used
to improve deficiencies in hospital schools at the time, and eventually
spearhead the movement toward collegiate nursing education.

The Advancement of Nursing Science, Research and Theory

World War II offered a role expansion for nurses, brought more
visibility to the importance of nursing as a profession, and provided
educational opportunities for women who had served in the war. In
the post-World War II period, the *Serviceman's Readjustment Act of
1944*, known as the G.I. Bill, allowed nurses returning from the war to
utilize benefits toward acquiring a college education. At the end of the
war, around 70,000 nurses were eligible to utilize funds from the G.I.
Bill.[69] With an increase in nurses obtaining baccalaureate, master's and
doctoral degrees in fields such as education, sociology, and psychology
under the G.I. Bill, the early 1950s began to see a sudden burst of activity
in the areas of research and theory among nurses who pursued higher
education. This period was especially marked by an interest in nursing
research and its effects on nursing practice. Two key figures at this time
were nurse theorist Hildegard Peplau and nursing researcher Virginia
Henderson. Both women cited Esther Lucile Brown's report of 1948 as
an influence on their work. This new body of knowledge in research and
theory would impact nursing education greatly. It legitimized nursing

[69]Davidson Baer, 54.

as a unique academic discipline, further justifying the move toward a collegiate nursing education environment wherein nursing scholarship could be supported and advanced.

NURSING IN THE ACADEMY: A SHIFT TO COLLEGIATE EDUCATION

"Every profession is influenced by its heritage, its immediate problems, emerging societal trends, the nature of its practice, and the extent to which it can realistically enact changes which will permit progress."

– American Nurses Association First Position on Education for Nursing, 1965

Well into the 1960s, the majority of nurses received their education from diploma schools. However, a movement that began in the early 1950s signaled a turning point and spurred a debate. This would begin with the popularity of associate degree programs for nursing, and culminate in the controversial 1965 American Nurses Association (ANA) position statement on baccalaureate nursing education.

The Rise of Associate Degree Programs

In the early 1950s, nurse academic Mildred Montag introduced the concept of the two-year associate degree program. The rise and popularity of associate degree programs in nursing can be attributed to social factors of the time, including marriages and baby booms in the post-WWII era. All of these social factors contributed to a large number of inactive nurses and thereby resulted in a workforce shortage that was much higher than other female-dominated professions. The community college setting fulfilled the need for rapidly turning out associate degree (ADN) educated nurses to work in hospitals. The ADN option was attractive to students for a few reasons – it was less expensive than diploma schools and the burgeoning baccalaureate programs, and of shorter duration than either. In addition, ADN programs began attracting more males and minorities to nursing. Yet the associate degree programs sowed seeds that would come to divide nursing. Montag envisioned two categories of nurses – the technical nurse who was a semi-professional, working under supervision; and the professional nurse who exercised more independence and autonomy in nursing practice. Associate degree graduates would fulfill these technical positions, while baccalaureate-prepared nurses would be most well-suited for the professional positions.[70] So, where did the diploma educated nurse fit in? This debate between "technical" and "professional" created a divide in nursing, especially among diploma school graduates who considered themselves professionals, not a second-tier class of nurse. This divisive debate over what it means to be a nurse, and how one's educational pathway defines the appropriate entry into nursing practice – technical or professional – would become heightened in 1965 with the publication of the ANA's First Position on Education for Nursing.

The ANA Position Statement of 1965

The 1960s were a time of revolt, reform, and liberation. Nurses were in the midst of vast social change. They were visible and active participants in civil rights and women's liberation movements that swept the nation during these exciting, yet often turbulent, times. Hundreds of nurses participated in the March on Washington in August 1963 as part of the Medical Committee for Civil Rights. In 1964, the *Nurse Training Act* was signed by President Lyndon B. Johnson which provided federal support for the recruitment and preparation of nurses, including those from minority groups.

The year 1965 was a watershed moment in the history of nursing education. When the ANA issued their *First Position on Education for*

---

[70]Malka, 31-33.

Nursing in the December 1965 issue of *The American Journal of Nursing*, it stirred mixed emotions among the nursing community. Some were strongly in favor of its advocacy for baccalaureate nursing education, some were strongly against. The position statement was grounded in the historical foundations of previous recommendations made by the *Goldmark Report* of 1923 and the *Brown Report* of 1948. It also reflected the educational trends and movements of the 1960s and the attention brought to the status of women's work and education by the feminist movements. The growing complexity of the healthcare system and nursing practice also influenced the position statement. After World War II, nursing had become more specialized and technologically advanced, requiring nurses to obtain competency in scientific and critical thinking.[71]

Prepared by the ANA Committee on Education, the 1965 position statement set forth the following recommendations:[72]

1. "Education for those who work in nursing should take place in institutions of learning within the general system of education"
2. "...minimum preparation for beginning professional nursing practice at the present time should be baccalaureate degree education in nursing"
3. "...minimum preparation for beginning technical nursing practice at the present time should be associate degree education in nursing"

The ANA position statement did not fall on deaf ears. The reaction was intense, both in nursing and medicine. Since it was published in

---

[71]Rosemary Donley and Mary Jean Flaherty, "Revisiting the American Nurses Association's First Position on Education for Nurses: A Comparative Analysis of the First and Second Position Statements on the Education of Nurses," *Online Journal of Issues in Nursing* 13, no. 2 (2008): 106-111.

[72]"American Nurses Association First Position on Education for Nursing," *The American Journal of Nursing*, 65, no. 12 (1965): 106-111.

The American Journal of Nursing, a platform accessible to many nurses, the audience was far-reaching. After all, this was the original purpose of *The American Journal of Nursing* when it was founded in 1900 – to serve as a forum of discussion and encourage the exchange of ideas in nursing, while promoting discourse on the nursing profession and nursing education. Yet, as historian Susan Malka points out, it was not the 1965 position statement alone which led to a steady decline in diploma schools.[73] Several other factors were at play, most notably the feminist movement and the desire to move nursing out of the perceived patriarchy of the hospital and into the autonomous environment of collegiate education, an environment where nursing could develop as its own academic discipline, grounded in research and theory.

Nursing Diploma Schools in Decline

The 1965 ANA position statement planted the seed for a decline in hospital-based diploma schools, as more colleges and universities began offering the Bachelor of Science in Nursing (BSN) degree. Perhaps most importantly, however, the demographic and image of nursing began to change starting in the 1970s. By the early 1980s, the National League for Nursing reported that enrollments in nursing schools had fallen by ten percent. This factor has been attributed to the impact of feminism that led to greater numbers of women seeking careers in nontraditional fields outside of nursing and teaching. Around this time, female enrollment in medical schools began to increase. As a result, in order for nursing schools to survive dwindling enrollment, massive recruitment campaigns were launched to attract nontraditional students, including men, to the profession.[74] Traditional hospital-based diploma programs experienced difficulty adapting to this changing environment.

For a century, nursing diploma schools in hospitals had established

---

[73]Malka, 56-60.

[74]Ibid., 65-66.

an identifiable and traditional nursing culture based on symbolism, ritual, and community. White uniforms, capping and pinning ceremonies, strict rules, nurses' dormitories, the reciting of the Nightingale Pledge – these would soon become a fondly remembered legacy of the past. Nursing was also becoming increasingly diverse. It was no longer a female-only profession of unmarried, single women. Therefore, it was essential that nursing education adapt to the sociocultural changes of the late twentieth century. By the 1960s, some nursing schools in hospitals had begun to end their strict rules, including the ban on married students. Nursing schools were finding it essential to abandon remnants of the traditional student nurse culture in an effort to maintain a secular and neutral identity in an environment of increased diversity and inclusion. The socialization of the student nurse that had become such a defining element of hospital-based nursing education since the early 1870s was no longer adaptable to the changes in the nursing profession and society as a whole.

According to 2014 statistics from the National League for Nursing, diploma nursing programs represented only four percent of registered nurse programs in the United States.[75] This percentage is expected to decline even more. Today's prospective nursing students have many educational options on the path toward becoming a registered nurse. Entry to practice can be obtained via the ADN or BSN degrees, as well as graduate-entry MSN programs, and less commonly the diploma program. Opportunities for advanced education abound, most notably with the Doctor of Nursing Practice (DNP) degree option which has been on the rise within the last ten years. The roots of these nursing programs lie within the educational legacy of hospital-based nursing diploma programs.

---

[75]National League for Nursing, "Percentage of Basic RN Programs by Program Type: 1994 to 1995 and 2003 to 2012 and 2014," http://www.nln.org/newsroom/nursing-education-statistics/nursing-programs.

LEGACY, HERITAGE, MEMORY

The 100-year-plus history of hospital-based nursing education in the United States is filled with stories of pioneers, leaders, and innovators who believed strongly in the unique role of nursing as a caring profession within the healthcare system. The history of nursing diploma schools coincides with the history of American nursing itself. The professionalization of nursing was only possible through the development and standardization of nursing education in these hospital-based schools.

Nursing education developed alongside major social, cultural, and historical events of the late nineteenth through twentieth centuries. The post-Civil War era made it apparent that trained nurses were desperately needed to provide safe patient care in expanding hospitals. The early nursing schools created their own legacy in notable graduates such as Isabel Hampton, who modernized nursing education and set the foundations for the professionalization of nursing. Early feminists, suffragettes, and public health advocates, most notably Lillian Wald, created new roles for nurses as social change agents through the power of caring. The Great Depression and the two world wars resulted in nursing shortages that forced nursing education to reexamine and scrutinize itself. The post-World War II era up through the civil rights and women's liberation movements of the 1960s and 1970s dramatically changed the image and demographic of nursing during a time of revolt and reform. As nursing education moved into collegiate settings, diploma schools began to decline.

The history of any significant movement is characterized by change, and hospital-based diploma schools certainly were not strangers to change. In fact, change and reform characterized these early schools from their very beginnings in the early 1870s. The progression of hospital-based nursing education in the United States laid foundations for the current educational opportunities available today in nursing. These historical foundations remain strong through the power of legacy, heritage and memory.

In Toledo, Ohio, eight hospital-based nursing schools existed from the founding of the Toledo Training School for Nurses in 1893 until the closure of the St. Vincent Hospital School of Nursing in 1999. The histories of these eight schools provide a rich patchwork of nursing memories from their alumnae and faculty. Similar to the friendships that existed among early nursing leaders Isabel Hampton, Mary Adelaide Nutting, Lavinia Dock, and Lillian Wald, the close friendship of the five authors of this book has led to the creation of a written testament to the legacy, heritage, and memory of the origins of nursing education in Toledo. The lessons, insights, and wisdom behind these stories will serve to inspire readers and light the path for future nurses.

Chapter 1
Wanting...To Be A Nurse

"My daydreams were of hospitals and I visited them whenever I could...I thought God called me to serve Him that way."

– Florence Nightingale

CHOICES: HOW DOORS TO NURSING OPENED

When young children are asked what they want to be when they grow up, their responses can be charming, amusing, insightful, and ambitious—princess, Batman, ballerina, firefighter—and nurse. What about those who grow up and choose nursing as a career? Why would one choose nursing?

Until the 1950s, cultural norms, values, and societal beliefs meant women had few options when it came to a profession. During the first half of the nineteenth century, women were expected to marry or choose a religious vocation. A woman working outside the home was considered quite unacceptable and nearly forbidden.

For society to accept "lady-like" women into the profession of nursing, many transformations had to take place. Nursing needed to develop from an apprenticeship trade into a profession. Modern nursing began in the 1860s with Florence Nightingale. Before her reforms, paid nursing suffered a reputation as a job for poor, often elderly women. Nursing was not regarded as work for "good women." The popular image was one of drunkenness, bad language and a casual attitude to patients.

In their 1907 book, *A History of Nursing*, Mary Adelaide Nutting and Lavinia L. Dock described the "dark times for nursing," from the

1600s to the 1850s, when qualifications of women who cared for the sick were questionable at best. "During this time the condition of the nursing art, the well-being of the patient, and the status of the nurse sank to an indescribable level of degradation. The only requirement to be a nurse was … that they are not confirmed drunkards."[1]

After Nightingale completed her nursing work during the Crimean War, she took what she learned and in 1859 published *Notes on Nursing: What it is and What it is Not*. In 1860, she opened the Nightingale Home and Training School for Nurses at St. Thomas' Hospital in London. The school was dedicated to communicating the philosophy and practice of its founder.

In 1873, the first United States nurse training program based on the principles of Nightingale opened at the Bellevue Hospital School of Nursing in New York. It operated until 1969.[2] Just as the first Nightingale-modeled nurse training programs were being established on the east coast, changes in population growth in the United States affected health of the population, influencing the development of hospitals and the need for trained nurses.

These factors also influenced events in Toledo, Ohio. At the end of the nineteenth century, Toledo was well on its way to becoming a prosperous Midwest manufacturing and agricultural center. Its location on the Great Lakes and as a transportation hub to Chicago and points west led to rapid growth. Immigrants from all over the world moved to northwest Ohio to work in the burgeoning automotive, glass, and petroleum refining industries. Drainage of the Great Black Swamp beginning in the 1850s provided fertile farmland, and agriculture thrived. Population growth was astounding. In 1890, the population in

---

[1]Lavinia L. Dock and Mary Adelaide Nutting, *A History of Nursing: The Evolution of Nursing Systems From the Earliest Times to the Foundations of the First English and American Training Schools for Nurses*. Volume 1. (New York: G.P. Putnam 1907).

[2]Colleen Bradley-Sanders, "Bellevue Hospital School of Nursing," Lillian and Clarence Se La Chapelle Medical Archives at New York University Health Sciences Library, http://archives.med.nyu.edu/collections/bellevue-school-nursing.

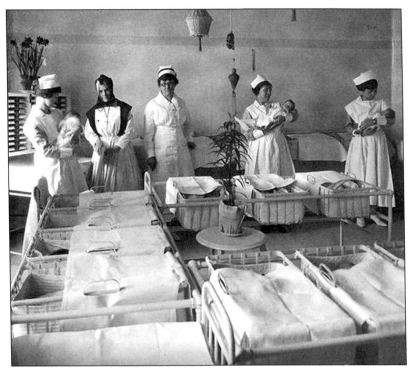

The Grey Nuns founded the first hospital in Toledo, Ohio in 1855. Here several nurses as well as a Grey Nun attend to babies in 1922.

Toledo was 81,434, a nearly three-fold increase from the 30,137 reported just 20 years earlier.

Although these manufacturing and farm jobs provided an improved lifestyle for many, they also contributed to sickness and injury. A cholera outbreak in 1854 was especially noteworthy; typhoid and milk sickness were endemic. Death and disability from manufacturing and farm equipment was common. It was the cholera epidemic that led a local Catholic priest to request a hospital be built in Toledo to "raise orphans and care for the sick."

Care of the sick and injured was becoming modernized in the United States. Knowledge of germ theory, asepsis, and anesthesia for pain-free surgery supported the need for a hospital. In 1855 the Grey

The first graduating class of the Toledo Training School, 1895, dressed in their handmade uniforms, smiling proudly on their momentous day. (Photo courtesy of Promedica Toledo Hospital Archives)

Nuns of Montréal opened the St. Vincent Asylum and Hospital in a two-story home on Superior Street near Cherry Street, in Toledo. It was the first Catholic hospital in Ohio. The mission was to care for the ill and orphaned, and nurses were needed to care for ill patients.

The Toledo Hospital Association opened the Toledo Training School in 1893. It was the first diploma nursing program in Toledo, and graduated five nurses in 1895. This school later became Toledo Hospital School of Nursing. The St. Vincent Hospital School of Nursing opened soon after in 1896.[3]

In the first decade of the 1900s, a continuing immigration boom,

---

[3]Editor Barbara Floyd, "Medicine on the Maumee: A History of Health Care in Northwest Ohio. An Exhibition," in *Ward M. Canaday Center for Special Collections, University Libraries/College of Innovative Learning*, ed. The University of Toledo (Toledo, Ohio: University of Toledo Press, 2012).

crowded living in urban centers, and an increase in birth rates had a negative impact on the health of men, women, and children in Northwest Ohio. The Great Black Swamp's humid summers and harsh winters provided a breeding ground for water and soil-borne diseases, and the increase in population density provided a perfect situation for contagious diseases to spread. Infectious disease was a frequent cause of illness and death. Farm life and the growth of manufacturing led to a rise in traumatic on the job injuries. The ill and injured could now go to hospitals for the latest in medical treatment and procedures.

From 1854 until 1908 in Toledo, 13 hospitals or infirmaries were built to care for the general and special populations (such as orphans, unwed mothers, and the mentally ill.) Eight of those hospitals subsequently established diploma nursing training schools. Between 1893 and 1999, these eight diploma programs graduated over 13,000 men and women who were qualified to take the Ohio nursing licensing examination to become registered nurses upon graduation.

From the time it opened until it was closed in 1988, the Toledo Hospital School of Nursing graduated 2,860 students. Opened in 1896, the St. Vincent Hospital School of Nursing lasted the longest and produced the most graduates, closing in 1999 after graduating 4,415 students.

The Maumee Valley Hospital School of Nursing was originally part of the old Lucas County General Hospital. Established in 1905, the school's name changed as the hospital's did, becoming the Lucas County Hospital in 1931, and finally the Maumee Valley Hospital in 1944. The school graduated 800 students before closing in 1972.

The Robinwood Hospital School of Nursing was established in 1905, and later became the St. Luke's Hospital School of Nursing in 1951. It closed in 1954, having graduated 484 students. The Flower Hospital School of Nursing was established in 1909 as the Flower Deaconess Hospital School of Nursing. The name changed a year later, and the school went on to graduate 1,110 students before closing in 1977.

The Mercy Hospital School of Nursing graduated 2,921 nurses while it was in operation, from 1918 to 1994. The Toledo State Mental Hospital School of nursing was open from 1919 to 1948, but records as to the exact number of graduates are unavailable.

The Riverside Hospital School of Nursing opened in 1921, and was originally part of Maternity and Children's Hospital. In 1927 it was renamed the Women's and Children's Hospital, and subsequently became Riverside Hospital in 1945. It closed in 1974, having graduated 629 students.

WHY BECOME A NURSE?

Availability of higher education and the acceptability of nursing as a profession for women were important social changes that influenced many to become nurses. The environment in Toledo contributed to the growth and development of excellent diploma schools of nursing.

The graduating nurses from Robinwood Hospital in 1916. By last name, they are, from the left, Reusch, Keller, Swartz, Sipes, Babiore, Bowser, and Schultz. (Photo courtesy the Toledo-Lucas County Public Library, Images In Time).

Graduates of Toledo's diploma nursing schools describe varied personal reasons and circumstances for entering the profession of nursing. Their reasons varied, but fell into four categories: inherent knowledge, family influence, exposure to an influential role model, and perceived limited career choices.

Inherent Knowledge

Many nurses interviewed shared that they always wanted to be a nurse, even from an early age. They said it was something inside of them that was "just known."

"I cannot remember ever not wanting to be a nurse. When I was about eight I had an appendectomy at Williams County and the nurses would let me sit at the desk with them. I loved it. Somehow, I realized that one of the options was a diploma program so I sent away for free brochures from all the Toledo schools when I was in the eighth grade. I applied to both Flower and Toledo and was accepted by both ... big decision!"

Rebecca Rayle Haberkamp
Flower Hospital School of Nursing, Class of 1968

"I always wanted to be a nurse; since the age of three per my parents. My mom's best friend was a nurse, (I loved the uniform and cap). My mom said she always wanted to be a nurse. (She may have influenced me along the way.) My ever practical father wanted me to do something that would support me and a family, if needed. Wise man. I also worked as a candy striper at Maumee Valley Hospital. I was in love with the whole medical field; so many options, opportunities and places to work as a nurse. I chose Flower, and have never regretted my profession or choice of training. I have been blessed being a nurse."

Anita Boardman Bersticker
Flower Hospital School of Nursing, Class of 1972

"I knew I wanted to be a nurse all my life. I was given a 'nurse kit' by my Aunt Barb. It seemed I always knew I wanted to be a nurse. Career night at Whitmer High School convinced me."

Linda Graver Lucas
Toledo Hospital School of Nursing, Class of 1984

Family Influence

Family members' health care experiences played a role in some nurses' decision to enter the profession.

"I think my Dad and Mother influenced me. My Dad was a marine in WW 2 and spoke highly of the Navy nurses that cared for him in a naval hospital. My mother often spoke of her mother, my grandmother, and how she kept a basket with home remedies, bandages, salves etc. and the neighbors called her when illness or injuries happened because she worked for a doctor and learned first aid. She liked caring for people."

Karen Steinmetz Christian
Maumee Valley Hospital School of Nursing, Class of 1968

"My aunt, a nurse, was always at our house telling us stories about her nursing experiences – these fascinated me."

Barbara Halpin Adamczak
St. Vincent Hospital School of Nursing, Class of 1958

"I wanted to be a teacher or an actress. About the time of my high school graduation my grandmother had a stroke. I wanted to know about that and how to help her. After graduation, I worked in a cardiologist office for one year, and then a podiatrist office for four years before starting nursing school. My mother-in-law was a nurse and encouraged me to go to school to be a doctor or a nurse."

Annette Mazzurco Hallet
St. Vincent Hospital School of Nursing, Class of 1984

"When I was a child my grandmother was diagnosed with amyotrophic laterals sclerosis. My mother and her sisters cared for her until her death one year later. This experience made me want to be a nurse."

Sandy Coldiron Choate
Flower Hospital School of Nursing, Class of 1972

Exposure to an Influential Role Model

Some nurses were inspired by an emotional or spiritual experience that led them to nursing. Being exposed to a touching patient experience, or watching a caring nurse, proved influential for many diploma graduates interviewed.

"When Dr. E.O. Christ, Toledo District Superintendent, visited some Methodist churches near Toledo, Ohio, he asked the pastor at the McClure Methodist Hospital, Reverend Burger, if he knew of a couple of girls he could get to join the new Deaconess Hospital (later known as Flower Hospital) and nursing school in Toledo. This resulted in two local girls, Miss Ina Johns and Miss Edith Philpot, being referred to nursing school."[4]

"My father was affected by mustard gas in World War I. He had hemorrhages from the throat or lungs. A public health nurse helped my mother care for him. She was from the Veterans Administration, I think. She had a navy blue uniform and a little black bag. From that point on, I thought I would like to be a nurse."

Alene Duerk
Toledo Hospital School of Nursing, Class of 1941

---

[4] Hazel Smith and Ruth Reis, "Flower Hospital School of Nursing 1909-1977," (Toledo, Ohio: Flower Hospital, 1986).

"I thought I wanted to be a teacher or a dental hygienist until I became a candy striper. When I walked in to the hospital that first afternoon after school I felt like I was home. I loved watching the nurses. I loved how the nurses treated people … I had to become a nurse like them. One nurse was sitting by an elderly gentleman feeding him slowly and talking softly to him … it really impressed me. I decided that is what I wanted to do."

Mary Ann Graves
Flower Hospital School of Nursing, Class of 1972

"I may have been influenced by several hospitalizations as a very young child. While living in Toledo, I attended Monroe Street Methodist Church, so Flower Hospital was a logical choice. My mother was a patient in Flower while I was in high school and I was extremely impressed with the care she received, especially from one of our Flower graduates."

Sandy Frye Eastep Lohmeyer
Flower Hospital School of Nursing, Class of 1964

"My uncle's niece was a nurse and was beautiful. When I was 12 years old, I saw her calmly take a fish hook out of her husband's foot and I was so impressed. She went to St. Vincent Hospital School of Nursing and so that's where I went."

Suzanne Mary Alexander Owen
St. Vincent Hospital School of Nursing, Class of 1974

"I received a gift at Christmas when I was five, a doctor's kit. I was fascinated with the stethoscope. I tried out candy striping at St. Vincent's. I worked with a Licensed Practical Nurse on a medical-surgical floor, who was a true mentor."

Norma Provencher Lake
St. Vincent Hospital School of Nursing, Class of 1974

48

"We were required to do community service hours at St. Mary's, my high school. I did about 400 service hours. I sat with patients. I comforted them. I was a candy striper, but I wanted the education to do more. There were no nurses in my family, but my 'Search for Values' teacher, encouraged me. She told me, 'You seem to like people and they like you.'"

Kaye Lani Rae Rafko Wilson
St. Vincent Hospital School of Nursing, Class of 1985

Perceived Limited Career Choices

As compelling as family and role models could be on a young woman's desire to enter the nursing profession, social values also played a part in her career choices. Opportunities were often limited to traditionally female-dominated careers such as a teaching or working as a librarian, cosmetologist, or secretary.

"I was told by my teacher in 6th grade that we needed to pick a career. At that time, in the late 1950s, I understood my sole choices were to be a teacher or a nurse. I did not want to be a teacher, so nursing it was. I read every Sue Barton and Cherry Ames book I could find to prepare, and loved them."

Debbie Fritz
Flower Hospital School of Nursing, Class of 1969

"It was after the Depression. I had to get an education to earn a living. I had an affinity for caring for others. My school of nursing did not charge tuition, so I went there and became a nurse."

Virginia Williams Whitmore
Lucas County Hospital School of Nursing, Class of 1943

"My parents and almost everyone else thought I should be a nurse but I was set on being a cosmetologist, even taking business courses my

first two years of high school. We compromised by my going to Penta County High School and taking cosmetology classes there. If I did not like it I could still go into nursing. I liked it but my skin was too sensitive to all the solutions we had to use. I had to learn facial anatomy in one of my classes and loved it. So I decided that maybe nursing was the answer and went back to my home high school. In my senior year, I took all my classes needed to get into nursing."

Mary Depner Beam
Flower Hospital School of Nursing, Class of 1973

"I always wanted to be a doctor. But, after being discouraged by everyone from the TV repairman to my family doctor, I decided to be a nurse. It turned out to be a decision that I would never regret. Bedside nursing is very fulfilling."

Glenda Drewyor
Flower Hospital School of Nursing, Class of 1969

QUALIFICATIONS TO ENTER NURSING SCHOOL

On the training of nurses, Florence Nightingale said, "My principle has always been: that we should give the best training we could to any woman of any class, sect, paid or unpaid, who had the requisite qualifications, moral, intellectual and physical, for the vocation of a nurse."[5] Admission requirements for nursing school in Toledo varied greatly during the twentieth century, yet the criteria remained remarkably similar. They included: character, level of education, age, gender, race, marital status, religious affiliation, personal health, and health requirements.

Character

Nightingale valued character, believing that only a self-disciplined

[5]Barbara Montgomery Dossey, *Florence Nighingale: Mystic, Visionary, Healer* (Springhouse, Pa: Springhose Corporation 2000).

50

Ads of the day heralded the benefits of a career in nursing, including an "interesting and respected career" that is also "the best preparation for marriage." Circa 1950s.

person could be a good nurse. To attest to moral respectability, nursing school applicants were asked to provide letters of recommendation indicating proof of good character. Often a character reference from either a pastor or another religious leader was required. These testaments were typically corroborated through an interview with a member of the admissions committee. The St. Luke's Hospital School of Nursing bulletin from 1952-1954 required successful nursing applicants to have "a fine character with personality traits and attitudes basic to the successful practice of nursing."[6]

Beth Kaltenbach Wilhelm, graduate of the St. Vincent Hospital School of Nursing, class of 1973, remembered she and her mother had a face-to-face interview with the school's director: "I couldn't tell if she thought I was good enough for admission. She talked to us and thanked us for coming. She told my mom that she might 'take a chance on me.'"

Level of Education

Nursing schools in Toledo required a specific baseline education. Starting in the 1920s, every nursing program required a high school diploma for entrance. In 1924, the admissions requirements of Robinwood Hospital School of Nursing stipulated that the applicant must have graduated from high school in the upper third of their class.

A well-rounded high school curriculum was required starting in the 1950s. Nursing school catalogues often listed the desirable high school credits that an applicant should achieve before entrance to nursing school. These requirements included successful completion of high school English, mathematics, a laboratory science, social studies, and a foreign language. Until the 1950s, suggested courses additionally included typing, home economics, music, and art.[7]

Science and mathematics requirements became more rigorous in

---

[6]St. Luke's Hospital School of Nursing, "St. Luke's Hospital School of Nursing Bullentin," (1952-54).

[7]"St. Luke's Hospital School of Nursing Bulletin," (1906-1949).

the 1960s. Students applying to St. Vincent Hospital School of Nursing in 1970 were required to have graduated in the upper third of their high school class and have taken biology, chemistry with laboratory, three units of mathematics, and four units of English. Physics was strongly recommended.

Age, Gender, Marital Status and Race

Although surprising by today's standards, admission requirements through the 1950s often stipulated limits on age and marital status. At the time, the suitable candidate for nursing training was a female, neither too young nor too old, generally between 17 and a half years and 35 years of age. Until the end of World War II, the Ohio State Board of Nursing required graduates to be 21 years of age or older to sit for the Ohio Board of Nursing Licensing Examination. Consequently, it was common for some graduates to wait months to take the State Board Exam until they turned 21.

The preferred candidate was single, never married or widowed. It was not until the late 1960s that every Toledo diploma nursing school accepted married applicants. The St. Luke's Hospital School of Nursing bulletin in the 1940s stated: "Marriage during the first 30 months of the program necessitates the student's withdrawal from the school." The school reserved the right to request "immediate withdrawal" of anyone who married while in the program.[8] At the time, unmarried women were more desirable for nursing as they could be more easily controlled, had no outside demands on their lives, and could work at will in the programs.

Maumee Valley Hospital School of Nursing was the first to break the prohibition on married students, allowing their admission in the mid-1950s. In the 1960s, most schools permitted marriage during the last

---

[8]Ibid.

year, however the student's wedding could not interfere with clinical or classroom obligations. Until the 1960s, and even later for some schools in Toledo, nursing students had to ask for permission from the director of the school of nursing to marry and live outside the nursing school dorm.

Pregnant nursing students were often told that they could not attend graduation. This was especially true if her pregnancy was obvious. These rules were relaxed after 1975, although nurses who graduated before that time remember them all too well. All these rules have their origin in Nightingale's desire to educate the most upright and moral women. Pregnant women, even married ones, did not meet that criterion for most of the twentieth century in Toledo diploma schools of nursing.

Male students were denied admission to many of Toledo's diploma nursing programs until the 1970s. Maumee Valley Hospital School of Nursing led the way, and admitted the first male student in the 1950s, according to E. Wanda Foltz Quay, who was an administrator in the school at that time. Carol Manley Singer, a 1961 graduate of the Toledo Hospital School of Nursing, was a faculty member at St. Vincent Hospital School of Nursing in the late 1960s. She recalls that men were not accepted into nursing programs most often due to the faculty's concern that patients would not accept a man as their nurse. Once men were admitted to Toledo diploma nursing schools, they enjoyed clinical and academic success. The ability to meet nursing standards, rather than gender, quickly became the focus of faculty and peers.

Race was not specifically mentioned in Toledo schools' admission requirements after the 1920s. However, it was not until 1948 that Mary Booker became the first African-American student to be admitted to a school of nursing in Toledo. Mary applied to multiple schools of nursing in Toledo over a two-year period before St. Vincent Hospital School of Nursing agreed to accept her application and granted her admission.

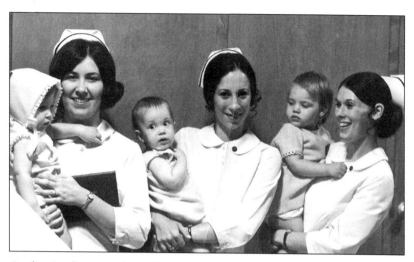

Graduating from nursing school was always a milestone in a nurse's career, but holding their baby made their smiles even brighter, ca. 1970's. (Photo courtesy Luanne Kaiser).

"When I got married and pregnant in 1966, Toledo Hospital School of Nursing, where I started and where I had received excellent grades through one senior year rotation, did not allow me to continue. Maumee Valley Hospital School of Nursing was the only area nursing school that accepted married students. So, I finished my nursing education there."

Sandy Crunkilton Pirwitz
Maumee Valley Hospital School of Nursing, Class of 1968

Religious Affiliation

Religious affiliation of the candidate was important for some schools of nursing. Sixty percent of Toledo diploma nursing schools were affiliated with a specific religion. The Methodist church sponsored Flower Hospital School of Nursing. Robinwood Hospital, now St. Luke's, was supported by the Lutheran Church, while St. Vincent and Mercy Hospitals were Roman Catholic. Riverside Hospital was affiliated with the Episcopal Church.

Although no Toledo diploma schools required students to be members of a specific church, many, such as Riverside, St. Vincent, and Mercy required a letter from the candidate's clergy. For a time, Toledo Hospital and Riverside Hospital Schools of Nursing indicated that the candidate should be Christian. Even secular or public hospital schools of nursing included religious aspects to important ceremonies.

Health Requirements

Admission requirements also addressed the personal health of the candidate, including ensuring applicants were strong enough to provide physical care. Candidates were required have a physical examination, completed by a physician and a dentist. St. Vincent Hospital School of Nursing required "the teeth must be in perfect condition,"[9] while Robinwood Hospital School of Nursing asked for a certificate from a dentist certifying condition of the applicants' teeth. Recent vaccinations were necessary, and the type of vaccinations needed varied dependent on historical context and the availability of vaccines. Pertussis vaccine became available immediately before World War I, diphtheria and tetanus prior to World War II, and the polio vaccine was made available and required for nursing school students in the 1950s. Measles, mumps, and rubella vaccines were required beginning in the 1970s. The smallpox vaccine was required until 1971.

Until antibiotics became widely available, nurses were well acquainted with the impact of infections and communicable diseases on patients of all ages. Protecting the nurse from infection by providing a clean environment and any existing immunizations was important. Diploma schools considered nursing to be a physically strenuous profession. The Americans with Disabilities Act of 1990 further opened the doors to nursing schools to qualified applicants, requiring accommodations for candidates with physical disabilities.

---

[9] "St. Vincent Hospital School of Nursing Bulletin," (1924).

ENTRANCE EXAMS AND OTHER CANDIDATE ASSESSMENT PROCESSES

School admission committees reviewed student applications. Membership on admission committees varied as nursing became recognized as an autonomous profession. The presence of physicians and hospital superintendents gave way to an all-nursing faculty group. Over time, the application process grew beyond a paper application. Every school of nursing required a face-to-face interview. In addition, Toledo, St. Vincent, Mercy, and Flower Hospital Schools of Nursing also required entrance exams. St. Luke's Hospital School of Nursing and Toledo Hospital required psychological or psychometric testing. Data from these standardized, knowledge, skills, and personality trait tests were used to help schools determine the applicant's aptitude for nursing.

"My interview was conducted by Sr. LeDuc, director, in her office. My mother was also there. I felt comfortable with the interview as Sister put you at ease."

Barbara Halpin Adamczak
St. Vincent Hospital School of Nursing, Class of 1958

"I remember the entrance exam was very difficult. We had to talk with the Director of Nursing and my mom was present also. Apparently, I did not do that well the second time around with the entrance exam, but Sister Mary Sylvia, the director, said she would give me a chance."

Kathryn Curley Bishop
Mercy Hospital School of Nursing, Class of 1967

"When interviewing at Toledo Hospital we had to see a psychologist. He tested and interviewed us. At Toledo Hospital School of Nursing, there was a long application and essay. I believe I also interviewed with Miss Klinger at the school in her office. Though the setting was pleasant it was

intimidating too as Miss Klinger was a formidable figure."

Karen Steinmetz Christian
Maumee Valley Hospital School of Nursing, Class of 1968

"I also applied at The Toledo Hospital, and had to take a psychological test with a psychologist interview. It included a vocabulary and ink blot test. During the testing, the psychologist asked me to draw a picture of a person and then proceeded to quiz me about the person. I remember worrying afterward that I seemed immature because the person I drew was in her early teens. There was an interview process also at Toledo Hospital with a couple of people. … I also remember taking a special exam for nursing school. They did not accept the other college entrance exams. I'm assuming it was some sort of (National League for Nursing) exam. This was required for both Flower and Toledo Hospitals Schools of Nursing but Toledo Hospital had the additional psychological testing."

Rebecca Rayle Haberkamp
Flower Hospital School of Nursing, Class of 1968

COSTS OF A NURSING EDUCATION

Upon acceptance into a diploma school of nursing, students had to transform their goal of wanting to be a nurse into a reality by finding ways to finance becoming a nurse.

The 1924 St. Vincent Hospital School for Nurses bulletin addressed allowances for nursing students. Following completion of the probationary period, "an allowance of eight dollars per month is granted each nurse during the first year." The monthly stipend, intended to cover the costs of books and other incidental expenses, was increased two dollars per year during the program. The stipends were discontinued at the start of the Great Depression in 1929.

Social and professional changes led to tuition and other charges for nursing school. Costs increased for hospitals and students when student nurses were no longer viewed as hospital staff. As accrediting organizations began to require specific classroom and clinical content, experienced nurses with higher educational qualifications were hired as faculty. A decrease in clinical hours to allow for increased theory content also decreased the hours that the hospital could depend on student nurses to staff the nursing units. This required hiring registered nurses in the place of students.

The common student expenses included tuition, books, clinical uniforms including shoes, caps, and capes, as well as equipment needed for clinical work, such as a watch with a sweep second hand, and later, a stethoscope. Some schools provided the required health assessments while others required the student's personal physician and dentist to conduct them, increasing the costs for students. Some costs were one-time expenses and others were ongoing.

The Lucas County Hospital School of Nursing was the only school that did not require tuition or other expenses. This hospital provided charity care for people in Toledo who had no means to pay. Although a public institution, Lucas County Hospital's supervisors were nuns who were registered nurses. Student nurses provided the clear majority of nursing staff for the hospital. According to Virginia Williams Whitmore, Lucas County Hospital School of Nursing class of 1943, students only had to buy their shoes.

Those who desired higher education but could not afford college often looked to nursing school. Tuition at a diploma nursing school was approximately one third the cost of a baccalaureate degree. This is largely because college tuition was only required for those programs which affiliated with a college or university for physical and social science courses. Costs to take the clinical nursing courses were subsidized by the hospital. A school of nursing provided a hospital with an ongoing stream of skilled professional nurses. Subsidizing nursing education was recruitment money well spent.

Federal funding for nursing education began in 1935 with provisions in the Social Security Act that provided financial assistance for nurses studying public health. Additional federal funds for nursing education were provided in 1946 with the Hill-Burton Act and during nursing shortages in the 1960s and 1980s. Students in Toledo also benefited from community scholarships.

The Hill-Burton Act

During the late 1940s and early 1950s, federal funding to hospitals, nursing homes, special hospitals, and rehabilitation facilities increased dramatically. The Hill-Burton Act of 1946 provided loans and grants to build hospitals and allow states to plan for other needed health care facilities based on community needs. A hospital building boom further contributed to a demand of professional nurses. [10]

Hill-Burton also provided funds for nurse education to support the growing need for trained professional nurses. For hospitals to qualify for Hill-Burton funds, they had to promise to provide emergency care to anyone regardless of ability to pay and to provide available non-emergency care to anyone who had the ability to pay regardless of race, color, national origin, creed, or any other factor unrelated to the person's ability to pay. In this way, the Hill-Burton Act laid groundwork for the Civil Rights Act of 1964.[11]

Nurse training funds were also in other legislation in the 1950s. Title II of the Health Amendment Act of 1956 set up provisions to enable traineeships for RNs to engage in full time studies in administration and education.[12] Nursing shortages continued to occur periodically

---

[10]B. Cherry and S.R. Jacob, *Contemporary Nursing: Issues, Trends and Management, 3rd Ed* (New York City: Elsevier Health Sciences, 2005).

[11]Timothy G. Smith, "Policy Perspective on the Entry into Practice Issue," *The Online Journal of Issues in Nursing* 15, no. 1 (2010).

[12]J.K. Leavitt and M.W. Chaffee D.J. Mason, *Policy and Politics in Nursing and Health Care, 5th Edition* (New York: ElsevierHealth Sciences, 2007).

throughout the twentieth century. In 1963, the U.S. Surgeon General's Consultant Group on Nursing identified that the nation was experiencing a nursing shortage. Their recommendations led to the enactment of the Comprehensive Nurse Training Act of 1964. This act provided funds for training programs and construction projects. Grants for education, loans, and traineeships were included. This program markedly enhanced the quality of nursing education, and was considered a major factor in the push to move entry into nursing practice to the collegiate setting and outside the hospital setting. [13]

Toledo became a hub for automobile manufacturing during World War II, including Jeep, General Motors, and Chrysler. Unions representing these skilled labor workers were supportive of higher education and offered nursing school grants annually. Community social clubs and service organizations often provided scholarship money for nursing students. Banks such as Toledo Trust and People's Savings and Loan allowed co-signed loans for higher education. Local hospital auxiliaries also provided scholarships or low interest loans for nursing students who met qualifications. Scholarships from student's churches were common. For example, when Robinwood Hospital School of Nursing closed, St. Luke's Hospital annually offered scholarships to Lutheran student nurses who applied and were students in good standing at any accredited nursing school.

TOLEDO SCHOOLS OF NURSING RESPOND TO THE CALL FOR NURSES DURING WORLD WAR II

War altered the supply and demand for nurses. Civilian needs took a back seat to the need for nurses to care for soldiers injured during combat. Several factors converged in World War II to create a perfect storm for a nursing shortage, beginning with competing demands for

[13]Ibid.

civilian and military nurses.

Job opportunities for women in business and industry, civil service, and women's military services competed for the same pool of potential employees that schools of nursing were trying to tap. To meet the need for more nurses during the war, the U.S. government enacted the Nurse Training Act of 1943, more commonly known as the Bolton Act. This legislation established the Cadet Nurse Corps, which gave nurses free training in exchange for commitment to military service.

The Bolton Act

The Bolton Act, sponsored by Ohio Representative Francis Payne Bolton and Senator Josiah W. Bailey of North Carolina, mandated that participating diploma nursing schools accelerate their programs from the traditional 36 months to 30 months or less. Available experience during the junior cadet period was shortened and redundancy during the senior year was eliminated.

The law established a new Division of Nurse Education under the U.S. Public Health Service, headed by Lucile Petry. These nurses were part of a special nurse corps, not "regular Army."[14] Funds appropriated from the Bolton Act provided scholarships, small monthly stipends, and uniforms for all students in the Corps. Students wore the school's uniform when working in their school setting. Additional funding was designated for postgraduate and refresher programs. Eligible students agreed to serve in the military or "essential civilian" nursing until the war's end.

Schools of nursing had to be accredited by the state or territory in which the school was located. Schools certified that the student was physically fit for nursing service and had met scholastic and other school standards. Ohio ranked fourth among 48 states in number of students

[14]Lilian Petry, "U.S. Cadet Nurse Corps: Established under the Bolton Act," *American Journal of Nursing (AJN)* 43, no. 8 (1943).

Students in the Cadet Nurse program perform drills on the front lawn of University Hall, at the University of Toledo in 1943. (Photo Courtesy Ward M. Canaday Center for Archival Collections)

graduating under the Cadet Nurse Corps. More than six percent, or 8,043, U.S. Cadet Corps Nurses completed diploma nurse training in Ohio.[15]

In Toledo, the U.S. Nurse Cadet Corps program was centrally administered by the University of Toledo, in conjunction with area hospitals. Students took biological science courses at the university and nursing classes at the hospitals. They also participated in intensive basic military training and prepared for deployment. Toledoans could observe drill practice in front of University Hall on the University of Toledo campus under the direction of O. Garfield Jones, professor of political science and WWI veteran.

Toledo Hospital is credited with training 29 nurses under the Bolton Act, although Flower Hospital School of Nursing was an active participant in the program as well. [16] [17]

"In our senior year of Nursing School we had the option of joining the United States Cadet Nursing Corps (USCNC), a branch of the service formed for the use of nurses in Army-Navy Hospitals, or serving in our own hospitals. I joined and elected to stay at Flower Hospital

[15]James H. Rodabaugh and Mary Jane Rodabaugh, *Nursing in Ohio: A History* (Columbus, Ohio: The Ohio State Nurses Association, 1951).

[16]Bulletin of the University of Toledo. (May 1944). Centralized Program in Nursing Education for the U. S. Cadet Nurse Corps at the University of Toledo., *University of Toledo bulletin* (1944).

[17]Philip A. Kalisch and Beatrice J. Kalisch, "Nurses in American History: The Cadet Nurse Corps in World War Ii," *American Journal of Nursing (AJN)* 76, no. 2 (1976).

where I spent my time in obstetrics. After graduation, the war ended and the USCNC was put out of force."

Mary Unger Krill
Flower Hospital School of Nursing, Class of 1946

"The majority of our class of 1946 joined the Cadet Nurse Corp. I believe we had the option of staying at Flower at least six months after training or signing up for this time at one of the Armed Forces Hospitals. Andy (Kathryn Anderson (Bertram) Ramlow), and I signed up for our last six months elsewhere. We were sent to the Chicago area to Vaughn Army Hospital and Hines Veterans Hospital, both located at the same base. This was quite an experience as both hospitals were very large compared with Flower. We made many friends from around the country."

Naomi Crow Layman
Flower Hospital School of Nursing, Class of 1946

Nurses shared their unique stories about how they came to enter a diploma nursing school in Toledo. The choice of which diploma nursing program was best depended on the viewpoint of the future student nurse. Some wanted to attend the school where a family member graduated, for others, a school's religious affiliation that was important. A few reported that geography was a factor in selecting a nursing school, as being close to home or close to public transportation was necessary. Some reasons were more emotional than logical, as when nurses reported choosing a school of nursing because it gave off "good vibes," "was the best in the area," or "had a great reputation." Competition between the schools was fierce. Even though the Toledo diploma schools of nursing all offered an excellent nursing education, most graduates will assert that their school is best.

"My aunt graduated from Toledo Hospital School of Nursing. She was horrified that I went to Maumee Valley Hospital School of Nursing.

64

She said, 'Maumee Valley nurses are workers, Toledo Hospital nurses are leaders.' I never regretted my decision and certainly do feel as though I was prepared to be a leader in our profession."

Elaine Studer Hetherwick
Maumee Valley Hospital School of Nursing, Class of 1966

Regardless of the reasons for selecting a school of nursing, once a woman or man was admitted, their life as a student nurse began. Each story, while encompassing shared experiences, was personal and unique to the student. Along the way, many made great memories and friendships that have lasted decades.

Chapter 2
Acting...Like A Nurse

"Nursing is an art; and if it is to be made an art, it requires an exclusive devotion, as hard a preparation as any...It is one of the Fine Arts: I had almost said, the finest of Fine Arts."

— *Florence Nightingale*

THE DIPLOMA NURSING CULTURE

Until the 1910s, many women entering diploma nursing schools were in their mid-20s and 30s. The maturity and experience were considered important qualities for women to bring to the nursing field. A shift occurred during the years immediately preceding World War I. Since that time, the clear majority of first year diploma student nurses in Toledo were young women directly out of high school. In the latter half of the twentieth century, nursing schools accepted men along with married and second-career women. Regardless of age, the exceptional student nurse began with an accurate understanding of the nurse's role.

Nurses sometimes fondly recall learning about nursing from adolescent-targeted nursing fiction, such as the Cherry Ames and Sue Barton series.[1, 2] These books depicted student nurses as caring, fun loving, single young women who worked hard to please doctors and take good care of their patients. Ames and Barton endeared themselves to their patients and studied faithfully to achieve the important, yet often unclear, tenants of the nursing profession.

---

[1] Helen Wells, *Cherry Ames, Student Nurse* (New York: Grosset and Dunlap, 1944 and Springer Publishing Company, 2006, 1944; 2006).

[2] Helen Boylson, *Sue Barton, Student Nurse* (New York: Random House, 1936 and Signet Books, 1984, 1936; 1984).

Student nurses in these books were immaculately attired in crisp uniforms and distinctive caps that triggered respect in all settings where nurses cared for the sick and injured. Ames and Barton rarely engaged in the strenuous activity of patient care. Ignoring the realities of the profession, these books were more glamorous than factual.

Beginning in the mid-1960s, the feminist movement and the refinement of professional nursing organizations were reflected in Toledo diploma programs' curricula. The preferred terminology became nursing education rather than nursing training. Nurses were no longer considered merely part of the hospital's staff, but rather professionals who brought essential and unique knowledge and skill to their patients.

"No man, not even a doctor, ever gives any other definition of what a nurse should be – 'devoted and obedient' – This definition would do just as well for a porter. It might even do for a horse." [3]

Florence Nightingale, 1860

"I remember my first nursing class. The instructor put up a slide with a person studying and a horse jumping over a gate. She said, 'Never forget that you are receiving a nursing education here at Mercy, not nurses training. I can train a horse to do tricks and do what I say. You are going to be taught how to think and work hard to give patient care well.'"

Anita Kowaski Cygnor
Mercy Hospital School of Nursing, Class of 1991

To focus the development of professional nursing behaviors, student nurses in diploma programs were systematically enculturated. Practices from both the military and the Christian church influenced the approach to assimilation found in every Toledo diploma school. Nuns and monks are widely considered to be the first nurses and it is undeniable that

---

[3] Florence Nightingale, *Nursing: What It Is and What It Is Not* (New York: Appleton and Company, 1860).

medical and nursing knowledge has grown during wartime.[4]

To effectively teach student nurses to develop professional values and to think and act like a nurse, schools drew inspiration from Christian charity, hierarchical control, strict adherence to rules, and distinctive uniform attire showing a person's rank. Decision making in nursing school was controlled vertically. At the top were physicians, followed by nursing faculty, student nurses, and patients.

Unless a student nurse had experience in the military or the convent, the introduction to nursing school was often shocking. Most nurses recall surprise and some dismay, not only at the amount of academic knowledge and clinical experience required in diploma nursing schools, but also at the lack of control they had over their lives. Impressionable young women were ideal candidates for this indoctrination. Rather than become resentful, most diploma graduates came to believe that this system was critical in their preparation as nurses and to identify as a member of the nursing profession.

"There were many rules. Everything had to be done just so. I remember those square corners when learning bed making. My Nursing Arts instructor was very tough. I respected her for that."

Betty Spencer Lemon
St. Vincent Hospital School of Nursing, Class of 1958

"Instructors were never friends. They were always authority figures. If you wanted to question the knowledge of the instructor, you had better be very prepared."

Cathy Frame Jaworski
Toledo Hospital School of Nursing, Class of 1981

---

[4]Philip A. Kalisch and Beatrice J. Kalisch, *American Nursing: A History* (Philadelphia: Lippincott Williams & Wilkins, 2004).

"'The Patient's Chart is a Sacred Trust' was framed and hung in every patient room."

Mary Ann Shea Arquette
St. Vincent Hospital School of Nursing Class of 1941

"The first class in Fundamentals of Nursing emphasized that everyone we care for deserves our respect. That message never stopped. I can still hear the instructor emphasizing 'the dignity of man.'"

Beth Kaltenbach Wilhelm
St. Vincent Hospital School of Nursing, Class of 1973

Further borrowing from military and Christian traditions, symbols became important for role identification in diploma nursing. Significant symbols of diploma nursing included the nurse's school cap, the student uniform, the nurse's school pin, the Nightingale lamp, and the Nightingale pledge.

THE NURSE SCHOOL CAP

Perhaps no other symbol of nursing is as widely recognized as the nursing cap. The nursing cap originally had a practical hygienic purpose: to keep long hair out of the way during patient care. Germ theory continued to evolve, and hair was known to harbor microbes that could spread infections. In the late nineteenth and early twentieth centuries, caps were modeled after a nun's headpiece or coif and covered most of the head. Schools of nursing eventually individualized cap designs so that a fellow nurse would be able to identify a colleague's nursing school by looking at her cap.

During the first semester, some schools in Toledo required female students to wear a cap signifying to physicians and hospital staff that they were new to nursing and on probation. These were called "probie caps" and were worn until the student passed the first semester, when

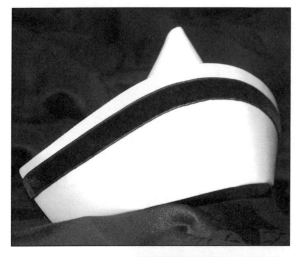

Mercy Hospital
School of
Nursing cap.

St. Vincent
Hospital School of
Nursing cap.

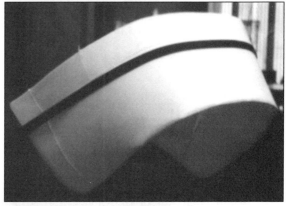

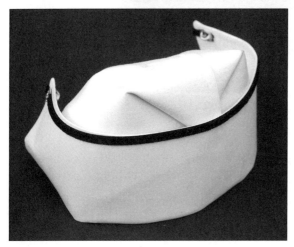

Flower Hospital
School of
Nursing cap.

probie caps were gratefully replaced with the school cap. The student would no longer be labeled as inexperienced. While probie caps may have been given to students as part of the school uniform during the first semester, student nurses had to earn the school cap. Although school traditions varied slightly in Toledo, to be awarded the school cap, students were usually required to successfully complete the first semester. This accomplishment was no small feat. In the mid 1960s, probie caps were abandoned. Without a probie cap, first semester freshmen simply attended the clinical experiences with their hair pulled up off the collar of the student uniform.

In the first semester, the student nurse typically took two or more college or university courses in the physical and social sciences, Anatomy and Physiology, Microbiology, Chemistry, Sociology, and Psychology. They were also required to take an introductory course in nursing, along with bedside skill training in a clinical laboratory and clinical experience in the hospital. A "C" grade average was required in the college courses. Similarly, at least a "C" in the nursing course and a satisfactory clinical grade was required in every diploma school in Toledo. Failing to meet these requirements resulted in dismissal for the student. The stakes were high, and not surprisingly, attrition rates were too.

A formal Capping Ceremony was held in recognition of students' success. These were solemn affairs, often held in the hospital chapel. Students were honored at a dinner or reception to commemorate the milestone. Students invited parents, friends, and significant people in their lives as witnesses. Speakers offered inspiring words reminding students of their special calling to care and serve. The director of the school or the student's "Big Sis," an upper level student assigned to informally mentor the freshman student, awarded the school cap. This recognition of her "Little Sis" carried a special acknowledgement of the student's achievement.

"Our ceremonies, like capping, were all moving and religious, at an Episcopal church. The capping ceremony was probably the most memorable because we became a S.N. This meant Student Nurse and students could sign their names that way in patients' charts."

Nancy R. Swartz
Riverside Hospital School of Nursing, Class of 1958

"I was very proud at capping. Now I had a real symbol of being a nurse. It was a big deal. Parents were invited to the ceremony. A student had to pass the first semester to receive a cap. The cap was hard earned."

Norma Provencher Lake
St. Vincent Hospital School of Nursing, Class of 1974

Proudly worn school caps were a sign of dedication to service and skilled care of the sick. Schools varied in how students' year or level was reflected on the school cap. School caps may have been worn plain white before graduation, but could be altered by schools to reflect class rank, reflecting freshman, sophomore, junior, or senior year of study.

Mercy Hospital School of Nursing placed either one or two diagonal black stripes on the cap, one for juniors and two for seniors. The Toledo Hospital School of Nursing had plain caps until the senior year when students were rewarded with a thin black stripe across the top of the cap. St. Vincent Hospital School of Nursing freshmen had plain caps, juniors had a thin gold band across the top of the cap, and seniors had a blue

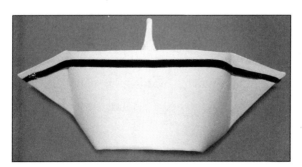

Riverside
Hospital School
of Nursing cap.

Toledo Hospital
School of Nursing
cap.

Robinwood Hospital
School of Nursing cap.

Maumee Valley
Hospital School of
Nursing cap.

The placement of the black band on the school cap followed a tradition. Here student nurses are guided by school director, Miss Klinger in the applying and securing the band. (Photo courtesy of The White Cap yearbook of the Toledo Hospital School of Nursing, 1965)

stripe. Riverside Hospital School of Nursing students wore diagonal green stripes.

Upon graduation, all schools of nursing in Toledo awarded graduates a black stripe to be worn across the top of the cap. A black stripe on a nurse's cap represented a registered nurse. There are varying ideas about the meaning of the black stripe. To some, the black stripe was an homage to Florence Nightingale. Reflecting the military and Christian influences on nursing, others recognize the stripe's military overtones, and the black and white contrast is also reminiscent of a nun's habit.

Caps became a less important part of the nurse's attire toward the end of the twentieth century. More men enrolled in nursing schools, requiring a change in tradition, as caps were gendered as feminine. School pins gained in importance as a symbol of a registered nurse. Nursing caps, once thought to be a sign of cleanliness, were found to be harbingers of disease-causing organisms.

Caps were not abandoned easily, however. Nurses, in conversation and in their literature, voiced their dismay with the disappearing caps, as did the public. Many nurses believed that, after the school pin, caps were the single most important symbol of their profession. Almost no nurse wears a cap now, and many programs no longer offer a cap. Yet, the nursing cap remains an important part of the history of nursing and an overt sign of the highly respected nursing profession.

THE STUDENT UNIFORM

Student uniforms were school specific, yet those in Toledo had some similarities. Uniforms were not pure white, as that color designated a graduate registered nurse. Student uniforms were short sleeved and required to be knee-length or longer. Many diploma school uniforms in Toledo were blue and white or green and white. Some had an attached or removable pinafore. This pinafore represented the aprons worn by the first nurses in the late nineteenth century. All school uniforms were collared. Male students typically wore white pants and a uniform top matching the color of the female student uniforms. Since men did not wear nursing caps, schools in Toledo followed the national trend, and started awarding chevrons or sleeve stripes. One, two, or three stripes were placed on the right sleeve of the male student to designate his level. Some schools also awarded uniform chevrons to female students as well.

The full student uniform consisted of the school uniform dress, or shirt and pants with appropriate chevrons, cap (for female students), polished white professional nursing shoes and white hose or white socks. The student uniform needed to be pristine every clinical day.

THE NURSING SCHOOL PIN

The tradition of the nursing pin originated with Florence Nightingale. Because of her service to the injured and dying soldiers during the Crimean War, she was awarded the Red Cross of St. George. In the 1860s, Nightingale chose to extend this honor to the most outstanding student nurses at St. Thomas Hospital School. By the early 1900s, all nursing graduates in the Toledo area were awarded school pins

Flower Hospital School of Nursing capping ceremony, circa 1966. (Photo courtesy of Promedica Toledo Hospital Archives)

as proof of their graduation from the school and to identify them as nurses.[5]

The pinning ceremony was an important part of graduation from a diploma nursing program, held during graduation or as a separate event. Roman Catholic diploma nursing schools, as well as others, held Baccalaureate, a religious service to honor the graduating class, where pinning could take place. Each diploma school of nursing in Toledo had a distinctive pin. The pin's design represented symbols of the hospital's mission and commitment to nursing.

Although capping ceremonies are now largely a part of nursing history, pinning ceremonies continue in almost all baccalaureate and associate degree schools of nursing in the United States. Nurses recall a feeling of awe during their pinning ceremony. The pinning ceremony was the real acknowledgement, perhaps more than the graduation ceremony itself, of graduates' admission into their profession.

"Receiving my pin at graduation was practically the most important event of my life."

Norma Provencher Lake
St. Vincent Hospital School of Nursing, Class of 1974

THE NIGHTINGALE PLEDGE AND NIGHTINGALE LAMP

The Nightingale Pledge

I solemnly pledge myself before God and in the presence of this assembly, to pass my life in purity and to practice my profession faithfully. I will abstain from whatever is deleterious and mischievous, and will not take or knowingly administer any harmful drug. I will do all in my power to maintain and elevate the standard of my profession, and will hold in confidence all personal matters committed to my keeping and all family affairs coming to my knowledge in the practice of my calling. With loyalty

---

[5]Terri Metules, "Pins and Pinning--the Traditions Continue," *RN* 61, no. 12 (1998).

will I endeavor to aid the physician, in his work, and devote myself to the welfare of those committed to my care.

In Toledo diploma schools, as in nursing schools around the world, the Nightingale Pledge was recited during both capping and pinning ceremonies. Florence Nightingale did not write the Pledge; rather, it was written in 1893 by a committee of nursing faculty from the Farrand Training School for Nurses in Detroit, Michigan, in honor of Nightingale's esteemed work caring for the sick and spearheading the modern education of nurses. Lystra Gretter, RN, leader of the original committee, revised the original version in 1935. The revised version is most often recognized today as the traditional pledge.[6]

The Nightingale Pledge was modeled after the Hippocratic Oath for physicians. The traditional Nightingale Pledge has faced criticism. Objections to the pledge include its outdated wording, reflecting inherent bias surrounding nursing practice, and the subordination of women, and especially, of nurses to physicians. Today, many versions of the pledge are available and nursing education programs use various versions. For nurses graduating from a Toledo diploma school, the traditional pledge was used. The nurse who recited the Nightingale Pledge promised to uphold the ethics, morals, knowledge, and clinical practice standards of the nursing profession. More than any other public acknowledgement, the pledge tied together the art and science of nursing. There are five sections to the pledge:

1. *I will pass my life in purity and to practice my profession faithfully.* These words stress the importance of making and keeping commitments, respect for the self, patients, and colleagues. Nurses must always strive to do what is right and trustworthy.

---

[6]American Nures Association, "The Florence Nightingale Pledge," (2016).

2.   *I will abstain from whatever is deleterious and mischievous and not take or knowingly administer any harmful drug.* This section highlights the nurse's commitment to staying well—physically, emotionally, and spiritually. This specifically includes a directive forbidding the nurse to take any harmful agents or to give medications or drugs to patients known to be harmful. Nurses' private ability to take care of themselves reflects their ability to care for others.

3.   *I will do all in my power to maintain and elevate the standard of my profession.* The nurse promises to continue education beyond nursing school, to refine and advance nursing skills. Nurses have the ability to change or influence professional standards and to exercise knowledge-based compassionate, physical care.

4.   *...will hold in confidence all personal matters committed to my keeping and all family affairs coming to my knowledge in the practice of my profession.* Even in the days before the confidentiality of patients' health information was legally mandated, nurses recognized that patients and families need the emotional security which comes when the nurse can be fully trusted to protect their privacy.

5.   *With loyalty will I endeavor to aid the physician in his work and devote myself to those committed to my care.* This section is most often cited as evidence that the Nightingale Pledge needs to be changed. Aiding the physician in his work is problematic both from a gender perspective, ignoring that men and women are both nurses and physicians, and when examining power structures, as physicians are not the boss of

nurses. Nurses are not handmaidens to physicians, nor are they subservient to them. However, this section also addresses the concept of nursing autonomy, implying personal freedom and the control over one's professional knowledge and skill. Nurses have the freedom to collaborate with physicians in their work and reciprocally, physicians with nurses in their medical work. This kind of autonomy allows the nurse to choose to serve the patient first.[7]

When the Nightingale Pledge was recited at capping and pinning ceremonies, nurses often held a ceramic lamp with a candle. The candle was lit as part of the ceremony to represent the lamp that Florence Nightingale used to make night rounds for the soldiers in the Crimean War. The lighted lamp represents the hope and both the literal and figurative light that nursing brings to the care of the ill and injured. Used together, the Nightingale lamp and Pledge serve as statement and representation of the deep-seated values and mission of nursing.

"The lighting of the lamps and the recitation of the Florence Nightingale Pledge were unforgettable. I still have a copy of the pledge hung in my dressing room."

Nancy R. Swartz
Riverside Hospital School of Nursing, Class of 1958

"Lamp lighting and the Nightingale Pledge occurred for us during capping at the beginning our second year. It was a very important time. A dinner was given in honor of this occasion and to recognize this accomplishment. I still have my Nightingale lamp and candle."

Cassandra Willey Zak
Toledo Hospital School of Nursing, Class of 1972

---

[7] Beth Heinzeroth McBurney and Tina Filoroma, "The Nightingale Pledge: 100 Years Later," *Nursing Management* 25, no. 2 (1994).

Promotion ceremonies were also an important part of the students' progress throughout the program. Students received a cap stripe or sleeve chevron to show their class level. (Photo courtesy of Mercy College of Ohio Archives)

Diploma nursing schools relied on symbols and a structured educational approach to teach the culture of nursing. Student nurses learned how to present an appropriate, professional appearance and clinical performance consistent with nursing standards. These symbols and procedures borrowed heavily from military and church influences. Diploma nursing graduates remember strict rules were followed to assure standardization in uniform and behavior. Ceremonies reflected the importance of symbols in the path to becoming a nurse. Although wearing nursing caps, uniforms, and school pins, and reciting the Nightingale pledge are not as large a part of nursing enculturation today, they remain a source of pride to diploma nursing graduates and respected symbols of nursing to the public.

Chapter 3
Living...Like A Nurse

"They should live in a home fit to form their moral life and discipline."

- ***Florence Nightingale***

THE NURSING SCHOOL RESIDENCE

An important part of a student nurse's socialization involved living with other student nurses in the residence or dormitory provided by the school. Until the late twentieth century, living in the school dorms was a requirement of diploma nursing students. This shared experience created a bond among class members, leading to many life-long friendships. These connections were reinforced over study hours, conversations about clinicals, romance, and even pranks.

"It was my weekend off and some of my friends were jealous because I got to go home for the weekend and I had a date. I left Friday and returned Sunday night just at curfew time which I think was 10 p.m. When I arrived at my room and opened the door, I found a totally empty space - the only thing left was the sink attached to the wall. No bed, no dresser, no desk or chair, no lamp, no clothes in the closet, nothing in my medicine cabinet, NOTHING. Down the hall behind closed doors I could hear the muffled laughter of my 'friends.' I found some of my belongings in the stairwell, some in the bathroom, and I don't remember where else. If I remember right, I do think my friends did eventually help me put my room back together, but they never did admit to the dirty deed!"

Martha Cook Firstenberger
Toledo Hospital School of Nursing, Class of 1966

The provision of room and board for nursing students dates back to the first Nightingale School in 1860 London. Nightingale had the novel idea to require that probationers live in a nurses' "home."[1] She believed in providing decent living quarters and board for students in exchange for the patient care provided in the hospital. Not only did this allow the students to be near the hospital and readily available when needed but also allowed for strict supervision of students in their extracurricular activities and study hours.

Nightingale was intent on reforming and elevating the status of the nursing profession. She feared that one instance of imprudent behavior, a false step, or showing lack of good judgment could set back progress for years. Consequently, students in her school were subject to stringent examination of clinical work, study habits, extracurricular activities, and personal character. Nightingale herself, along with the matron of St. Thomas Hospital, evaluated students on such characteristics as punctuality, quietness, trustworthiness, personal neatness, and cleanliness. Personal behavior deemed indiscrete, such as flirtation, was punished by instant dismissal. Young women selected for her school "must not allow themselves to be women; but their mission was to prove that the woman can be sunk in the nurse."[2]

Unlike other educational settings where students could leave to their home or living quarters to find time away from their teachers and peers, living in the nurses' residence demanded the individual always be in the student nurse role, as the dormitory allowed for close observation by faculty, house mothers, and fellow students.[3]

---

[1] Cecil Woodham-Smith, *Florence Nightingale* (New York: McGraw Hill Book Co., 1951).

[2] Ibid. pg. 234-236

[3] George Psathas, *The Student Nurse in the Diploma School of Nursing* (New York: Springer Science & Business Media, LLC, 1968).

DORMITORY LIFE

Early in the history of diploma schools in Toledo, living quarters for student nurses were often established in personal homes or rented properties close to their respective hospitals. In some cases, rooms were located within the hospital itself, which often included private homes that had been incorporated into hospitals. As dormitories were constructed, many provided single or double rooms for students, along with small suites where the nursing and dormitory directors and some graduate nurses could live.

The first diploma school in Toledo, the Toledo Training School, housed students for one year in the hospital or nearby homes. The following year, in 1894, the former Valentine H. Ketcham home at

In 1894, the former Valentine H. Ketcham home at the corner of Cherry and Bancroft was converted to the Toledo Training School, and nurses' residence. C. 1895 (Photo courtesy the Toledo-Lucas County Public Library, Images In Time).

Croxton House, the dormitory and school of the Toledo Hospital School of Nursing. (Photo courtesy of ProMedica Toledo Hospital archives)

St. Vincent's D'Youville Hall built in 1950. It was added to the 1917 Purcell Hall and both were used to house the school of nursing until its closure. (Photo courtesy of the Mercy Health/St. Vincent's archives)

the corner of Cherry and Bancroft was converted to the school and nurses' residence from its previous use as a hospital. There was a 12-bed dormitory on the main floor and upstairs rooms housed two to four students. Second and third year nursing students occupied the upstairs rooms. There were community bathroom and bathing facilities, but no kitchen.

After construction of the new hospital on North Cove Boulevard, the name changed from Toledo Training School to Toledo School of Nursing and then, Toledo Hospital School of Nursing. Students moved into a new school and residence hall, Croxton House, on Oatis Avenue over the 1929-1930 New Year's holiday. Croxton House was enlarged in 1942, and remained the residence for Toledo Hospital nursing students until the school closed in 1988. [4]

Other Toledo diploma schools had similar histories. St. Vincent Hospital School of Nursing students originally lived on the third floor of the hospital building until a new student residence, Purcell Hall, was built in 1917. In 1950, the school was expanded, adding a building named D'Youville Hall. It was dedicated in March of that year, and both buildings continued to be used until the school closed in 1999.[5]

Flower Hospital School of Nursing students, instead of living in one designated building, lived in many different structures over the years, with students spread out in multiple locations. They all were in the general vicinity of the hospital. Initially, they were housed in the Steven W. Flower Home on Collingwood Avenue, which was also the location of the hospital. Another class moved into the "Barnola," the carriage house of the Flower home, and still others into a home across the street that belonged to a private citizen. Over the years, as the hospital evolved, students occupied large and small homes and apartment buildings called Simms and Grace Halls. Simms Hall reportedly had at least one

[4]Paulette J. Weiser, *A Legacy of Caring: A History of the Toledo Hospital School of Nursing* (Toledo, Ohio: Wayne Graphics, 1988).

[5]Susan Cross, *St. Vincent Hospital School of Nursing Centennial History: 1896-1996* (1996).

apartment with nine students and one bathroom. Students also lived in a structure converted from a restaurant called the "Farm." It was not until 1966 when a dormitory was built on the hospital grounds that, for the first time, all nursing students lived together under the same roof. [6]

Other schools had more stable living arrangements. Until Hardee Hall was built in 1946, Riverside Hospital School of Nursing students lived in a building near the hospital that was remodeled in 1927. Hardee Hall was replaced with a new residence hall and education building in 1968.[7] Robinwood Hospital School of Nursing students lived in the Mabel Morrison Nurses' Home at 2521 Robinwood Ave., next to the hospital.[8]

Maumee Valley Hospital School of Nursing built the first dormitory for nursing students, Victorian Hall, in 1931 on Arlington Avenue alongside the new hospital. It included space for 70 nurses.[9] An addition was added in 1965. Joanna Grilli Anthony, Maumee Valley Hospital School of Nursing class of 1967 graduate, recalled being moved into a warehouse-like building for at least a month during the construction of the new addition. There were 12 to 15 students in a big room on cots, and one bathroom.

The "White House" was the name of the Convent for the Mercy nuns who came to Toledo. When the Mercy Hospital School of Nursing began in 1918, the White House was renamed St. Mary's Hall and became the classroom facilities and residence hall for the student nurses. As student enrollment increased, more buildings were added to house students. They included the Richardson Homestead on Collingwood

[6] Hazel Smith and Ruth Rees, "Flower Hospital School of Nursing Class of 1922," (Flower Hospital School of Nursing).

[7] "Riverside Hospital School of Nursing," ed. Riverside Hospital School of Nursing (Toledo, Ohio 1956-1957).

[8] St. Luke's Hospital School of Nursing, "St. Luke's Hospital School of Nursing Bulletin," *Bulletin* (1952-54).

[9] Editor Barbara Floyd, "Medicine on the Maumee: A History of Health Care in Northwest Ohio. An Exhibition," in *Ward M. Canaday Center for Special Collections, University Libraries/College of Innovative Learning*, ed. The University of Toledo (Toledo, Ohio: University of Toledo Pres, 2012).

Hardee Hall, the school and dormitory of the Riverside Hospital School of Nursing. (Photo courtesy of Riverside "Memories and Progress" by Riverside School of Nursing Alumnae Assoication, c. mid 1960's)

Mercy Hospital School of Nursing, c. 1957 (Photo courtesy the Mercy College of Ohio archives)

Avenue (added in 1937) and renamed McAuley Hall, and Madonna Hall on Madison Avenue. St. Patrick and St. Anne's Halls on Jefferson Avenue were added between 1937 and 1957. In September of 1957, a new school and dormitory was constructed to house all students.[10]

The Toledo State Hospital School of Nursing opened in 1919 and closed in 1948.[11] Students lived in a dormitory on the hospital grounds that continued to house affiliating students for many years after the school closed. Other affiliating institutions, such as children's hospitals, provided residence halls for students during out-of-town clinical rotations.

In all Toledo diploma schools, single or double rooms for students had beds, dressers, desks and desk chairs, and sometimes a sink. Students

[10] R.S.M. Sister Mary Consilium Moore, "A History of the Schools of Nursing Conducted by the Sister of Mercy of the Union in the Province of Cincinnati," (1964).

[11] Chantelle Coles-Neal, 2016.

The living room of the dormitory of Robinwood/St. Luke's Hospital School of Nursing. (Photo courtesy of St. Luke's archives).

A student dormitory room for two students. (Photo courtesy of Mercy College of Ohio archives)

could bring personal touches including a bedspread, rug, small radio, or a fan to make their rooms feel more like home and be more comfortable in hot weather. Community bathroom and bathing facilities were located on each floor, and some had kitchen areas. These kitchens were intended only for snacks, as all meals were taken in hospital cafeterias. The cost of the meals was included in the fees paid to the school of nursing.

Typically, the top floors of the residence halls were reserved for student living quarters, with administrative offices, the medical library, classrooms, clinical lab rooms and a diet kitchen found on the first and lower levels. In some schools, students changed rooms following a hierarchical system. For example, the senior students could move to a more desirable floor while the freshmen and junior students were relegated to the less desirable locations. In other schools, students kept the same room throughout the program. Dorms frequently included an area for recreation, with a pool table or similar games, and a TV when they became available. There was a living room area for receiving guests and most residences provided small rooms where students could entertain guests more privately. Most of those spaces did not have doors, however, and if they did, the doors were to remain open. Several dormitories had rooftop areas where students could sun bathe in nice weather. This was a popular pastime.

Some dorms had a room where sewing machines were available along with an ever-popular popcorn machine. Facilities for personal laundry were usually available.

Uniforms, towels, and bed linens were laundered by the hospital laundry and delivered back to the student once or twice a week. Students had to launder, starch, and fold their own caps, or make other arrangements, taking them to a professional laundry. Maintaining the

Popcorn was a popular snack. Here are students making popcorn in their kitchen, c. 1950's. Notice their dress. This was during the years that students were not allowed to wear slacks in the dormitory. (Photo courtesy of Mercy College of Ohio archives)

cleanliness and integrity of the cap was a frustrating challenge, especially for the schools with more elaborately folded caps such as Flower Hospital and Maumee Valley Hospital. These practices continued until uniforms became permanent press, and caps became obsolete. Before the permanent press uniforms, student uniforms required some assembly on each return from the laundry. This assembly was part of the students' ritual in preparation for clinicals.

"The hospital laundry did our uniforms. They were returned to us very stiffly starched. We used to say that we couldn't have fallen while wearing them because they were so stiff. It took several hours of wearing a uniform before you could feel comfortable."

Mary Ann Shea Arquette
St. Vincent Hospital School of Nursing, Class of 1942

"We'd hitch up our uniforms to our knees but they were supposed to be two inches below the knee. If they called inspection we'd lower our skirts. The hospital did our laundry, but we had to keep our linen closet in tip-top shape. To this day, I still have properly folded towels."

Virginia Williams Whitmore
Lucas County Hospital School of Nursing, Class of 1943

"The hospital laundered our bedding and uniforms. They were starched stiff. We put them together with safety pins and special buttons. They were so starched they would rub our necks and cause red irritation."

Barbara Rule Krochmalny
Flower Hospital School of Nursing, Class of 1970

Some nursing students were lucky to live on a campus that provided underground tunnels or walkways to pass to and from the hospital, a

Flower Hospital School of Nursing and dormitory, built in 1966, allowing for the first time, all students to live together under the same roof. (Photo courtesy the Flower Hospital School of Nursing 1967 yearbook, The Creed)

convenience during inclement weather and after nightfall; others had to brave the elements in their constant commuting.

"The tunnel from D'Youville Hall to the hospital was convenient in bad weather and since the hospital's neighborhood was not predictable after dusk, we usually felt safer using the tunnel. It ended right by the cafeteria which was always a good thing for us, especially on clinical mornings."

Beth Kaltenbach Wilhelm
St. Vincent Hospital School of Nursing, Class of 1973

"The dormitory was called Victorian Hall and there was a tunnel system for every building except our dormitory."

Elaine Studer Hetherwick
Maumee Valley Hospital School of Nursing, Class of 1966

"We were treated like adults at one end of the tunnel (that connected the school and dorms to the hospital) and like children at the other end."

Lynn Kitchen Langel
St. Vincent Hospital School of Nursing, Class of 1974

Until the 1950s, it was not uncommon for school administrators to live in the dormitories. In addition, a housemother managed the operations of the dormitory, and along with her assistants, monitored the front desk, took phone calls, distributed mail, ruled over the sign-in and sign-out book, and generally kept track of the comings and goings of the students and their dates 24 hours a day. There were also floor mothers who cleaned rooms and watched over the students on the individual floors As in the clinical area, students were always addressed formally by their last names in any communication. Student opinions of the house and floor mothers varied.

"The housemothers checked our rooms each night to be sure students were there. My friend used to grease the door knobs with coconut oil and use a coconut head and cape to scare the housemother."

Alice U. Calabrese
St. Vincent Hospital School of Nursing, Class of 1950

Maumee Valley School of Nursing Victorian Hall built in 1931 on Arlington Avenue.

"Our housemother was great. She never told on us when we snuck out of the dorm with shorts on under long raincoats (she knew)."

Betty Spencer Lemon
St. Vincent Hospital School of Nursing, Class of 1958

"The housemothers were stern and watched comings and goings, especially with boyfriends. They were 'parent subs.'"

Cathy Frame Jaworski
The Toledo Hospital School of Nursing, Class of 1981

When the student population was overwhelmingly young women just out of high school, moving into the dormitory was for many their first time away from home. Despite battling homesickness, friendships developed quickly among classmates and were often influenced by room assignments in the dorm and groupings for clinicals.

Nursing student Lynn Eurenius taking an outside call which was always a highlight of any day. She is sitting on the floor of the small telephone room. (Photo courtesy of the Toledo Hospital School of Nursing 1978 White Cap yearbook)

"It was exciting and scary to move into the dorm. I did not really know my roommate – I think we were assigned a roommate. She was from Sandusky, Ohio. She invited me to her home for a weekend and took me to Cedar Point. It turned out well – my roommate and I became very good friends."

Kathy Curley Bishop
Mercy School of Nursing, Class of 1967

The schedule of the nursing student did not allow for much time off for visits home, so communication with friends and family often relied on letters and the occasional phone call. Each floor of residence halls typically had one or two phones for nurses to receive calls, with some dorms only having pay phones. When a call would come in to the desk, the housemother would buzz the student's room through the intercom to notify the student of an outside call waiting. If she was not in the room, the call would go up to the floor phone, and whoever answered would yell out the name in the hallway to announce the call. Some phones were in a small room with a door, providing some measure of privacy. Students who received phone calls, especially if the call was from a boyfriend, were the object of envy and a favorite topic of conversation.

The first stop after clinicals on return to the dorm was always the mailbox; everyone hoped for a letter from home or a note in the mailbox that said they had had a call, c. 1957. (Photo courtesy Mercy College of Ohio archives)

Most students from small, rural communities communicated with their families via letters. Mailboxes were usually located on the first floor, close to the front desk, and were the first stop on returning to the dorm after clinicals or class. The mailboxes were also a mechanism to get school announcements to all students in a timely manner, but it was always a letter from home or a friend that was cause for excitement.

Common goals, shared experiences in professional and personal lives, and the amount of time spent in close proximity, created family-like

Almost all nursing schools affiliated with a university for their science courses at least by the 1950's. Few schools provided transportation. Hundreds of Toledo Hospital student nurses walked through Ottawa Park to get to and from The University of Toledo for classes, c. 1954. (Photo courtesy of A Legacy of Caring)

bonds among nursing classes. The dormitory was much more than a place for students to live while in school. The dormitory experience contributed enormously to the educational process as well. The following words of students will provide a good summary of what the dormitory experience meant to diploma nursing students.

"We learned to work together; we studied together and helped each other; clarified questions from classes etc. and became very good friends in the process. We still meet for lunch every month after 50 years!"

Barb Moellman
Toledo Hospital School of Nursing, Class of 1960

"My favorite memories are being a "probie, Charlene playing 'taps' on her trumpet at lights out, the basketball game with Providence Hospital School of Nursing in Sandusky, borrowing clothes, tanning on the roof, sneaking out and sneaking in, looking over the first floor railing

at our blind dates, the water fights, the feather pillow fights, and two one-o'clock late passes per month."

Betty Ann Brogle
Mercy Hospital School of Nursing, Class of 1962
50th Reunion Memories

"The best memories of nursing school days come from living nine girls to an apartment our freshmen year with all sharing one bathroom and a very small closet for four of us in the front bedroom. We learned to get along and tolerate each other and developed friendships that continue to this day. My classmates have been great friends and a support system for each other over the years."

Sue Maltman
Flower Hospital School of Nursing, Class of 1964

"My favorite memories of Mercy are when a whole group of us piled into the dorm room of another student to have a lesson explained that few understood. She was one of the most intelligent students and the youngest by two years."

Patricia Puhl Pfleghaar
Mercy Hospital School of Nursing, Class of 1965
50th Reunion Memories

"Living in the dorm with students initially unknown to me was instrumental in forming many lasting relationships. The environment was conducive to learning at many levels. We were exposed to things to help us develop educationally, mentally, and socially. The experiences at Toledo Hospital School of Nursing prepared me for life."

Sandra Franklin Holloway
Toledo Hospital School of Nursing, Class of 1966

RULES

Continuing Florence Nightingale's belief that the behavior of the nurse should be above reproach, dormitory rules were quite strict. This sampling of the House Rules of the St. Vincent Hospital School of Nursing of 1910-1919 offer a glimpse of what it was like during those very early years.

1. Rooms must be left in perfect order, beds well made, floors clean and furniture dusted. It is forbidden to lie on the white bedspread; when a nurse wishes to rest, it must be turned back

2. No excessive loud talking, laughing or singing on the floors of sleeping rooms. Do not forget the night nurses are sleeping

3. Screaming, whistling, and gum chewing are forbidden at all times and in all places.

4. It is forbidden to eat in sleeping rooms. The tea room and recreation hall are for eating.

5. You are strictly forbidden to take, borrow, or loan one another's clothes.

6. You are forbidden to visit one another's room. The tea room, roof garden, or recreation hall are reserved for social intercourse.

7. To attend all classes and lectures you must be in full uniform, including cap.

8. You must be properly attired to go to the first floor (no kimonos).

Overtime, some rules were relaxed, especially in relation to students' behavior in their residential space, but many rules remained. For decades students were required to be in full uniform to attend classes. As clinical and class hour schedules began to change, they were allowed to wear street clothes to class, but there were rules to be followed regarding street clothes too. For instance, members of the 1960 class of the Toledo Hospital School of Nursing recalled not being allowed to wear slacks unless they were leaving the building. Skirts were the expected attire. This was consistent across most all of the diploma schools and did not change until the mid 1960's.

"We had a strict dress code. I clearly recall the Director of the School scolding me for wearing culottes to class."

Karen Steinmetz Christian
Maumee Valley Hospital School of Nursing, Class of 1968

While dormitory dress rules relaxed over time, expectations for clinical attire and appearance were always high and continued to be so. Students risked being sent off the clinical unit to change if uniforms were rumpled, shoes were not polished, hose were not intact, hair touched the uniform collar, or the cap was not clean or well anchored on the head. Nail polish was prohibited, and jewelry was limited to a watch with a sweep second hand. If ears were pierced, only gold studs were permitted and no rings, other than a wedding band, were allowed.

"Our uniforms had to be below our knees. It was the 1960s for heaven's sake! Everyone else was wearing mini-skirts!"

Catherine Van Vorce Horner
Flower Hospital School of Nursing, Class of 1969

"Our appearance was very important. It was part of my preparation for clinical. Shoes polished white, clean, and ironed uniform, only gold stud earrings, no nail polish and hair up off the collar. A student would be

sent off the unit if not in full uniform. This could cause a failing grade for that day."

Cassandra Willey Zak
Toledo Hospital School of Nursing, Class of 1971

"Our uniform dresses had to be in the middle of the knee ... no shorter. We were told if our uniform was too short, we could be thrown out of the program."

Janice Smith Cook
Flower Hospital School of Nursing, Class of 1976

"One day I was disciplined for wearing my stethoscope around my neck while walking into the clinical unit. I was told it was "unprofessional appearance."

Anita Kowaski Cygnor
Mercy Hospital School of Nursing, Class of 1991

Students at most Toledo diploma schools were not allowed to be present on hospital patient units without wearing their full uniform. In-hospital clothing rules relaxed somewhat in the 1970s. A student was permitted to wear a school approved lab coat and appropriate attire on the nursing units to prepare for clinical experience, or other legitimate reason. Students were still required to wear a clean and pressed lab coat, and were prohibited from wearing jeans, any shoe that was not fully closed in the back and front, athletic shoes, short skirts, shorts, low cut blouses, or untucked shirts. Dangling earrings and other obvious jewelry was also considered inappropriate.

The importance of the student uniform and the consistency with which the uniform dress code was enforced cannot be overstated. An immaculate uniform was an essential sign to anyone in the hospital that the student was a professional. The student's appearance reflected the school's values and reputation. Nursing faculty noted the attention to detail in the student's appearance. Cleanliness and neatness were taken seriously as signs of commitment to excellent nursing care and of respect to patients and hospital staff. The dress code even counted toward the clinical grade.

Except for clinicals, whenever the student was returning to or leaving the dormitory, she had to stop at the desk to sign in or out. This required specifying the time she was leaving, time and date she expected to return, and general intention of her absence, such as a date or going home for the weekend. Every school had a curfew, usually around 10 p.m. The curfew time was exact, according to the housemother's watch, and not a minute after, with the dormitory door being locked at that time. If one missed curfew, there were consequences, ranging from receiving demerits or being "campused," or confined to the dormitory. Too many demerits or times of being campused could result in dismissal from the school. The rules were not something that most wanted to test. There were late passes available to students, extending curfew to 11 p.m. or midnight, and very occasionally until 1 a.m. These were limited in number, usually available only on the weekend and often had to be requested in advance.

"If you did not have any penalties, 9:45 p.m. was the curfew six nights a week and 11 p.m. on Sundays. It bears emphasizing that the time was exact, not a minute later. As happened at times, students might be walking up the flights of steps from the Emergency entrance (where the students entered and exited) and the housemother would lock the big door at the exact minute even if she saw you getting out of a car or coming up the steps. And there you stood, outside, until she came back from doing some checking. So now you were good and late and automatically lost your next Sunday night 'late.'"

Mary Ann Shea Arquette
St. Vincent Hospital School of Nursing, Class of 1942

"We had a 10 p.m. curfew, but some students put a block in the door so they could get in after curfew. If they got caught, they were grounded."

Sharon Kitchen Viers
Mercy Hospital School of Nursing, Class of 1966.

"I was 2 minutes past curfew one night. When I got to the dorm, the housemother was already on the phone with my mom. I was 20 years old!"

Kaye Lani Rae Rafko Wilson
St. Vincent Hospital School of Nursing, Class of 1985

Men were not allowed past the first floor of the residence halls except for move-in and move-out days. Any maintenance man was instructed to yell "man on the floor" when he stepped off the elevator to give the students fair warning to ensure they were appropriately attired to exit their rooms. Any visitors, especially dates, were met on the first floor.

Initially, students had to be single to enter the nursing program. Some schools allowed that students could marry in the last six months of their program or other specified period. That policy began to change when, for the first time in the mid-1950s, a married student was accepted into the Maumee Valley Hospital School of Nursing. E. Wanda Quay, director, helped lead the way in opening doors to male students as well. Acceptance of these "non-traditional" students also initiated changes in the required dormitory living policies.

"We were not allowed to be married while we were in school. My husband-to-be was about to be shipped out to the Pacific during World War II. On Easter Sunday, April 9, 1944, I had clinicals in the dietary kitchen in the morning. Then, I went to church and we were married privately after the services. It was just our family. No one said a word. Even though I was a senior and was to graduate the next month, I would have been expelled."

Lois Anspach Smith
Toledo Hospital School of Nursing, Class of 1944

"When we entered, we could not be married. That changed in 1958 when students could marry after the completion of the first term of the junior year. I had a vacation scheduled, so planned my wedding for that time. The school then wanted to change my vacation time, and threatened to campus me when I protested. In the end, reason prevailed, the wedding went on in March of 1958, and my vacation was restored. I was the first student to marry, and I also graduated on schedule."

Nancy R. Swartz
Riverside Hospital School of Nursing, Class of 1959

"To get married before I graduated, move out of the dorm and live with my husband, I had to interview with the Director, as well as another person ... I think it was a hospital Board member. They wanted to make sure that I was not going to get pregnant. My mother and the Director must have discussed dates regarding getting married and graduation and felt that I would not get pregnant by graduation. No one could be pregnant in school nor at graduation as women who were pregnant were not supposed to work. I also think they interviewed me rigorously because they were going to lose control over me. They would have no say in my hours of sleep, coming and going. I made sure I was on time for everything; I never was late for any class or for clinical. You had to prove yourself. You had to beg and grovel for permission to marry."

Bonnie Hummel Borgelt
Flower Hospital School of Nursing, Class of 1974

By the 1980s, the diploma schools in Toledo had changed their policy to accept married students and men. The male students were not allowed to live in the dorm, nor were married students with their spouse. Some schools helped male students to find living quarters. Some male students were provided housing on the hospital premises and others found their own living quarters. Over time, the rules changed, allowing all students to live outside the residence if desired.

Dorm rules also changed over time. In contrast to the 31 rules from the early years at St. Vincent Hospital School of Nursing, only six rules were in place in the 1980s. Still considered somewhat restrictive, they were:

1. No jeans, shorts, or shoes that do not cover the heel of the foot (i.e., no clogs)
2. Married students may not live in the dorm.
3. No coed floors in the dorms.
4. Closing hour for the dorm is 1 a.m.
5. Students may not leave the dorm after midnight.
6. Men are not allowed on the dorm floors.

While the rules would seem to create a constrained and protected environment by today's standards, they were precisely the reason many parents leaving their daughters for the first time felt comfortable in sending them to a diploma school of nursing.

A DAY IN THE LIFE

At the turn of the century there was little time for nursing students to do anything but work, sleep, and eat. St. Vincent Hospital reported student nurses in 1896-1899 worked 12 hours every day, including mopping and dusting wards, with a half day off per week. They had mandatory study hour from 8 p.m. to 9 p.m. and were to be in bed by nine. Schedules were regimented and left no room for flexibility.

Those on the day shift were to rise at 6 a.m., have breakfast at 6:30 a.m., report for prayer, roll call, and inspection at 6:50 a.m., and be ready to report for duty at 7 a.m. Students were not allowed to return to the dormitory while on duty. The schedule was similar at the Toledo Training School where study hour was 9 p.m. to 10 p.m., and lights out at 10 p.m. The door to the residence was locked at 10 p.m. St. Vincent

Hospital School of Nursing locked their doors at 9:30 p.m., and students had to have their baths taken before then. Lights out was also at 10 p.m. Daily chapel service was a requirement in most nursing schools, even those without a church affiliation, until the 1950s. Chapel was often before clinicals in the morning.

"The inexorable hour of 10:15 p.m. meant lights out. However, many of us had our own flashlights which we used under the sheets to continue to study."

Mary Ann Shea Arquette
St. Vincent Hospital School of Nursing, Class of 1942

"We always had 'lights out', but then we would braid hair and sit in the hall and talk where there were dim lights."

Virginia Williams Whitmore
Lucas County Hospital School of Nursing, Class of 1943

"We had lights out at 10 p.m. - we would put a towel under our door to block the light."

Judith Reitz Rudolph
Mercy Hospital School of Nursing, Class of 1963
50th Reunion Memories

As the years progressed, students were given more responsibility and accountability for their own time management. Arriving on time for clinicals, getting enough sleep, and studying became the responsibility of the student, not the housemother. This resulted in less structured days, with the exception of scheduled class and clinical time. Clinical hours decreased over time as well. The Goldmark Report of 1923 was instrumental in that it recommended the student workweek be limited to no more than 48 hours.[12]

---

[12]Josephine Goldmark, "Nursing and Nursing Education in the United States," ed. Committee for the Study of Nursing Education (New York1923).

"I felt like I was on vacation when my hours were decreased from 48 to 44 hours per week."

Barbara Driver Condon
The Toledo Hospital School of Nursing class of 1954

The clinical day could be an eight-hour shift, or four to six hours of clinicals in the morning and class in the afternoon. Through the 1950s, it was not unusual to have clinicals in the morning, class in the afternoon, and then return to clinicals for several more hours. Clinical assignments also occurred on the night shift as well as days and evenings.

"I remember working 11 p.m. to 7 a.m. and then staying up for class at 10 a.m."

Elaine Studer Hetherwick
Maumee Valley Hospital School of Nursing, Class of 1966

Prior to the 1970s, even if permitted, it was rare for a student to have a car. St. Vincent provided a bus to transport students to and from their classes at Mary Manse College, while Mercy students were expected to walk, and Maumee Valley students took public buses. Toledo Hospital nursing students recall the long walks across Ottawa Park to the University of Toledo in all kinds of weather. Hitchhiking back and forth, a practice not condoned by the school, was a common occurrence, as the community was quite aware of the students' long trek and frequently offered rides.

"The Nursing Superintendent told us that under no circumstances were we to accept rides to the University. We were to walk through Ottawa Park together."

Lois Anspach Smith
Toledo Hospital School of Nursing, Class of 1944

"We usually could fit five to a cab. It cost 50 cents each way."

Barbara Rule Krochmalny
Flower Hospital School of Nursing, Class of 1970

Beginning in the 1960s, more students had cars and would provide rides to their classmates. When cars were not available, Flower Hospital nursing students recall taking cabs to the University of Toledo.

St. Vincent students who did not have access to a car took public transportation when they affiliated with Lourdes College. When the new hospital was built in Sylvania, Flower Hospital purchased a bus to transport Flower students back and forth from the dorm on Collingwood Blvd.

ACTIVITIES AND TRADITIONS

Until the 1920s, student nurses had little time for recreation; however, they managed to squeeze in some opportunities for activities. Students from most schools related that they had a piano, along with a Victrola and records, where they could gather to sing. Many remembered taking walks in their hospital's neighborhoods. Sunbathing was a popular pastime in spring and summer. Some schools had tennis courts available, and of course, spending time in the dorms together was always popular. Students engaged in other sports such as croquet, volleyball, and softball.

From the beginning, Toledo diploma nursing schools promoted the development of a well-rounded nurse and woman. In the 1910s the St. Vincent Hospital School of Nursing stated it was their goal to produce a "cultured, well-educated woman." In keeping with that goal, they required 22 hours of French and 30 hours of elocution.[13] The Toledo Hospital School of Nursing, in the early 1940s, provided special tours of the Toledo Museum of Art, and tickets for Toledo Symphony concerts, the Town Hall series, and Repertoire Little Theatre performances. Most

---

[13]Cross.

schools, sometimes assisted by alumnae and hospital auxiliary members, provided dances and parties for their students and dates. Some schools provided lessons for such things as bridge, knitting, dancing, etiquette, social correspondence, menu planning, table decoration and setting, and current styles and appearance.[14]

Musical opportunities were created as well. St. Vincent had a student orchestra that played for graduations and cappings. All schools had choirs, which were sometimes mandatory, that performed at school functions. The Flower Hospital School of Nursing choir performed at Methodist churches in Toledo and surrounding small towns.[15] These musical activities began to disappear in the late 1960s and early 1970s as policies changed, and students were no longer required to live in the dormitories.

[14]Weiser.

[15]Hazel Smith and Ruth Reis, "Flower Hospital School of Nursing 1909-1977," (Toledo, Ohio: Flower Hospital, 1986).

Many schools provided opportunities for students to use their musical talents. This is the Mercy Hospital School of Nursing orchestra of 1959. (Photo courtesy of Mercy College of Ohio archives)

"We were called to the parlor to meet with a nun and informed we were volunteering for the St. Vincent Nursing Student Orchestra. We were assigned instruments and times to go to the Ursuline Academy Music Department for a series of lessons. We played for capping ceremony and graduation. We practiced one evening every week and unless you left the program, you were in orchestra until you graduated."

Mary Ann Shea Arquette
St. Vincent Hospital School of Nursing, Class of 1942

"When my supervisor found out I played cello, I was assigned to the 3 to 11 shift because she wanted me to play cello on Sunday mornings."

E. Wanda Foltz Quay
Robinwood Hospital School of Nursing, class of 1948

Most graduates of the Toledo Hospital School fondly remember the formal teas. The teas began in the 1930s and continued until 1988, when the school closed. They began as daily events, but eventually developed into a weekly and special event tradition.

"The dorm mother oversaw our weekly tea. We would all meet in our beautiful, paneled, thick carpeted living room on the first floor. We had changed into a clean apron and freshened up. She would pour tea or coffee from a lovely silver tea service while sitting at the head of a formal table. There were china cups and little cakes or cookies. We learned to make polite conversation and act like ladies."

Karen Steinmetz Christian
Maumee Valley Hospital School of Nursing, Class of 1968
(Started at Toledo Hospital School of Nursing and finished at Maumee Valley Hospital School of Nursing)

"I remember the Tuesday afternoon teas in whatever effort was going into making us into young ladies. We always went from the teas back to our rooms where our mischievous antics continued as usual!"

Carolyn Horn Welsh
Toledo Hospital School of Nursing, Class of 1966

Getting to know the upper classmen was a rather abrupt introduction when the tradition of freshman initiation began around the 1940s. Initiation rituals included such things as bedpan races on front lawns, scrubbing the floor with toothbrushes, and bowing to the upperclassmen. This description of the Official Probie Costume, to be worn on initiation night for the Toledo Hospital School of Nursing Class of 1966, gives an indication of why incoming freshmen did not always regard initiation as much fun, unlike the upper classmen: "The costume consisted of 'ratted' hair (not combed), a bone in hair (provided by the student's Big Sis), makeup on only half of the student's face, a different shoe on each foot, their father's shirt and boxer undershorts, nylons rolled down to their ankles, a Probie necklace (also provided by their Big Sis), and a pillow in a laundry bag."[16]

"I still remember the words to the Probie song! 'You are almighty senior/the epitome of perfection/look upon this miserable wretch/with a benevolent orb/I am a lowly probie/and I bow in supplication to you/ almighty senior.' It's funny today, but I felt silly at the time."

Catherine Van Vorce Horner
Flower Hospital School of Nursing, Class of 1969

---

[16]Martha Cook Firstenberger, 2016.

114

Formal teas, such as this one in 1944 in the living room at Croxton House, were a weekly and well known event at the Toledo Hospital School of Nursing. (Photo courtesy of A Legacy of Caring)

"Initiation was a three-day period when the upperclassmen had us do crazy things, dressing mismatched and ill-fitting outfits, and messed up our rooms."

Nancy R. Swartz
Riverside Hospital School of nursing, Class of 1959

"Initiation went on for a week, and some things continued for a whole month. We were at the mercy of our Big Sis and had to do things like wear beanies and bibs even to the hospital cafeteria, and we had to sing the probie song wherever we were when they asked. I remember we had to iron clothes for our Big Sis too. Initiation was stopped (by the school administration) shortly after my class."

Sharon Kitchen Viers
Mercy Hospital School of Nursing, Class of 1966

115

While initiation usually was not always fondly remembered, the Big Sis program at several schools was often regarded as supportive and helpful. A Big Sis was a second-year student assigned as a mentor to each incoming freshman.

"I didn't know anyone and had never been away from home for any length of time. Orientation was intimidating; I had no idea what to expect. My Big Sis helped me learn the ropes."

Norma Provencher Lake
St. Vincent Hospital School of Nursing, Class of 1974

"One item I really loved was the safety pin chain, made by our Big Sis, which counted down the months to graduation. You would take a pin off each month and put it on the bottom, so when you graduated the Cap with Black Stripe was on the top of the chain. Mine had tabs denoting the months and flags identifying important events, like Probie, Half Way, Junior and Graduation. There were paper caps for Capping and Graduation. Great memories!"

Christine Surratt
Flower Hospital School of Nursing, Class of 1971

Nursing students all decked out as clowns for the annual fall carnival, c. 1973. (Photo courtesy of ProMedica Toledo Hospital archives)

A timeline safety pin chain prepared by a Big Sis for freshmen Little Sis. It included a safety pin for every month in the program. Creative Big Sis's added visuals for special events such as capping, half-way mark and holidays to the corresponding safety pin. The chain was hung in the student's room and a safety pin was moved at the completion of each month to the "completed" column. It was a great visual of progress in the program, a good motivator to keep going, and is fondly remembered by many diploma graduates. (Photo courtesy of Martha Cook Firstenberger, Toledo Hospital School of Nursing, class of 1966)

"My Big Sis was very helpful with what to expect, old class notes, and study guides."

Cathy Frame Jaworski
Toledo Hospital School of Nursing, Class of 1981

In the 1940s and 1950s, student governments with committees to deal with such issues as dormitory life, recreation, social events, and fund-raising activities were created. Student Nurse Associations were established at the local, state, and national levels. These student organizations sent representatives to the local, state, and sometimes national Student Nurse Association meetings.

In the 1950s, St. Luke's Hospital School of Nursing student government consisted of "students of each class are organized with elected class officers and a faculty advisor. The entire student body is organized into a Student Association with Representative Council which has for its purposes regulation of dormitory living, planning of recreational activities and development of student interest in governmental and parliamentary procedures." [17]

Following creation of the student governments, student committees became responsible for coordinating many activities. An intramural basketball league with competition between the schools was a popular event. All diploma nursing schools in Toledo brought their choirs together to present an annual Nightingale Sing. The choirs sang in uniform, with many wearing their school capes in transit.

Student committees planned everything from parties, dances, movie nights in the auditoriums, holiday decorating of the residence halls, chapel services, and community projects. Individual creativity surfaced in such things as annual talent and variety shows, carnivals, holiday skits

---

[17]St. Luke's Hospital School of Nursing, "St. Luke's Hospital School of Nursing Bulletin," (1952-1954).

Basketball was a popular activity in the schools with intramural competition. This is the Maumee Valley Hospital School of Nursing basketball team of the 1960's. (Photo courtesy of Arlene Hustwick and Joanna Anthony)

The cover of the Toledo Student Nurses Association's Nightingale Sing program from Dec. 5, 1968, at Whitmer High School. The Master of Ceremonies was local TV station news commentator Lamont McLoughlin. William Ensign, the mayor of Toledo, delivered the keynote address, and the 1969 Toledo Student Nurse was also announced. Each school's choir performed a variety of selections, and at the end of the evening, they formed a mass choir to sing a song to end the program. A reception immediately following the event offered students from different schools the opportunity to meet and interact. (Copy courtesy of Penny Risher).

and a variety of other activities unique to individual schools. Producing the yearbook, a large undertaking, was also the responsibility of a student committee.

Some schools had a Mothers Club with mother-daughter banquets. Elaine Studer Hetherwick, Maumee Valley Hospital School of Nursing Class of 1966, recalled that her parents were part of a PTA-like group that helped with their graduation.

Candle lighting was a tradition that emerged in the 1960s and 1970s and became quite popular. It was an activity to recognize newly engaged students.

"I remember many parties and engagement celebrations. We would sit in a circle and pass a lighted candle around ... it would stop at the girl who just got engaged."

Kathryn Curley Bishop
Mercy Hospital School of Nursing, Class of 1967

Graduation time brought important traditional activities. In many schools, the junior class planned the Junior-Senior Banquet to honor graduating seniors. In nearly every diploma school in Toledo, the last clinical day for the seniors included the much-anticipated destruction of student uniforms. Some uniforms were burned in a big bonfire; others were cut and ripped in the hospital while still on duty, with the hospital staff getting in on the fun.

"On the last day, we burned our mended and greatly worn student uniforms and The Toledo Blade *newspaper captured a photo of the bonfire. It was an emotional cleansing prior to the actual celebration of graduation. Now we were moving on, wiser and much more skilled from when we entered."*

Betty Ann Brogle
Mercy Hospital School of Nursing, Class of 1962

This was the last clinical day for this group of graduating seniors. It appears not only were their uniforms shredded throughout the day as was customary, but they may have gotten unexpected showers too. (Photo courtesy of Toledo Hospital School of Nursing, White Cap yearbook 1986)

As the rules changed allowing non-traditional students, men, and older women, to enter the schools, and students to live out of the dormitory, the character of the schools changed also. While students still had the common goal of becoming a nurse, the relationships and bonds formed among classmates were not as strong as when the classes were more homogenous.

"Very few in my class lived in the dorm. I lived at home and commuted to school. I did work while in nursing school. I started as a nursing aide at Toledo Hospital, but quit after the first weekend as the hours were too many and the work was extremely difficult. Instead, I took a job at Franklin Park Mall. When I socialized during the years I was in nursing school, it was with high school and mall friends. I felt a closer bond to them than my nursing classmates."

Anita Kowaski Cygnor
Mercy Hospital School of Nursing, Class of 1991

"Most students commuted from home. There were lots of rules and curfew times in the dorm. So, we didn't spend much time in the dorm; we went home on weekends. When we were there, everyone had their own TV in their room and we spent a lot of time studying. I don't stay in touch with my nursing school friends."

Lissa Wilhelm Brehm
St. Vincent Hospital School of Nursing, Class of 1995

Chapter 4
Learning…To Be A Nurse

"What is training? We can't put into you what is not there. We want to bring out what is there. Training is enabling you to use the means you have in yourselves. Training is drawing out what you know yourselves. Learn your work thoroughly in your year of training. Store it up and practice it in your brain, eyes, and hands, so that you may always know where to find it, and these – brain, eyes, and hands – may always be your ready servants."

– Florence Nightingale

Nurses' opinions on the rigorous expectations of their diploma education varied depending on their progression within the program. Frequently, student nurses' descriptors made it sound like torture. New graduates usually said "I'm just glad I survived." But seasoned diploma nurses will invariably say their nursing education gave them the best preparation they could have ever wanted to begin their career in nursing.

What is a diploma school of nursing? What made it different? How did these programs evolve? What was the program of study like? Typically, diploma nursing graduates will say that it was the quantity of clinical experience and how their instructors made sure that theory or class content was correlated with each clinical experience that allowed this sense of beginning competence at the conclusion of their program.

"Classes were very hard and I was fearful of failure since I did not do well on the entrance exam. Fortunately my roommate was an excellent student and helped me to develop very good study habits and I did very well."

Kathryn Curley Bishop
Mercy Hospital School of Nursing, Class of 1967

"We lost one third of our class after the first semester classes. Those were Nursing Fundamentals and sciences at the University of Toledo. We had one instructor, Miss B., who acted like a drill sergeant, especially with medications. It always seemed like I had to do extra med cards."

Catherine Van Vorce Horner
Flower Hospital School of Nursing, Class of 1969

"I remember one student taking one of her first blood pressure readings on a 'real patient'. She applied the cuff very carefully, placed

Pathology.		11	80	Dr. Egle
Communicable Dis.	5	15	80	Dr. Berger
Surgical Nursing	8 3	10	70	Dr. Patrick
Pediatrics	3	14	83	Dr. Payne
Def in Disease	6	10	80	Miss Wall
Medical Diseases	4	13	85	Dr. Stifel
Orthopedic Surgery.		11	85	Dr. Wilson
Anesthesia		5		- Coletrap.
Ethics		9		Rev. E.M. O'Hare.
Gynecology	5	8	90	Dr. Doherty -
Nursing Methods	6	6	70	A.K. Breuer, RN
Ear, nose, throat	3	10	95	Dr. Effler

Portion of a grade book from Mercy Hospital School of Nursing from 1929. Physicians taught all of the content on diseases. Only one nurse is listed teaching "Nursing Methods". During this time period nursing education strictly followed the medical model when presenting information. (Mercy College of Ohio Archives) *the stethoscope, pumped the cuff to the right level, and then got this very panicked look on her face. She quietly whispered 'I can't hear anything'. I quietly whispered back, 'try putting the stethoscope in your ears.' She turned red, put the ear pieces in place and finished perfectly. Today she's an amazing oncology nurse. I always loved working with first level nursing students."*

Maria Nowicki
Mercy School of Nursing, Class of 1970
Faculty, Toledo Hospital School of Nursing 1980-1985
Faculty, Mercy School of Nursing 1986-1992

The curriculum at the diploma schools gives an insight into why the programs were so comprehensive, and in turn, difficult.

CURRICULUM

The plan of study or curriculum in a nursing program included the classroom activities, clinical experiences, evaluation methods, and all learning experiences that had to be mastered by each student to successfully graduate from the program. It was designed by faculty through careful planning with attention to state regulations, national accreditation standards, and current knowledge and trends in the profession. The curriculum was organized, specific, and detailed with regard to the requirements for completion.

Regulation and Accreditation

Visits from the Ohio Board of Nursing or the national accrediting association, the National League for Nursing, caused considerable angst among the faculty. A great deal of time and effort always went into preparing reports for these agencies, as well as time spent in interviews during the visit.

CAPS, CAPES, AND CARING

PROGRAM OF STUDIES OF MERCY HOSPITAL
SCHOOL OF NURSING--TOLEDO, OHIO 1961-1962[a]

Courses	Number of Hours				Percentage
	Per Year			Total	
	1st	2nd	3rd		
Biological & Physical Sciences				255	17.4
Anatomy	105				
Chemistry	60				
Microbiology	60				
Food and nutrition	30				
Social Sciences				190	13.4
Professional adjustments	15				
Psychology	30				
Religion	30				
Sociology	30				
Medical ethics		15			
Family relationships		15			
History of nursing		15			
Professional trends in nursing			30		
Community health & welfare	10				
Nursing & Allied Arts				1000	69.2
Basic nursing	170				
Pharmacology	50				
Medical-surgical nursing	190	95	105		
Nursing of children		105			
Obstetric nursing		90			
Psychiatric nursing			150		
Ward administration			15		
Diet therapy		30			
TOTALS	780	365	300	1445	100

[a]Mercy Hospital School of Nursing Catalog (Toledo, Ohio, 1962-1963).

Program of Studies, Mercy Hospital School of Nursing, 1961-62.
(Courtesy of Mercy College of Ohio archives)

"My first full time position in teaching was at a diploma school of nursing. I had the good fortune of starting as the faculty were preparing for an accreditation visit. I learned more about the program in a short time by the intensive review that took place than I could have ever learned in a year on my own. I thought it was great. Not sure the rest of the faculty felt the same way about it."

Maria Nowicki
Mercy School of Nursing, Class of 1970
Faculty, Toledo Hospital School of Nursing 1980-1985
Faculty, Mercy School of Nursing 1986-1992

Ohio Board of Nursing (OBN)

The Ohio Board of Nursing was established in 1915 as the Nurses' Examining Committee. In 1928, it became the Nursing Department of the State Medical Board. In 1941, it became an autonomous board, The State Nurses Board. In 1956, the name was once again changed and it became the State Board of Nursing Education and Nurse Registration. In 1988 the name was changed to its current title, the Ohio Board of Nursing (OBN).

The mission of the OBN is "to actively safeguard the health of the public through the effective regulation of nursing care." Part of this regulation is to oversee the nursing education programs in the state. The Board reviews requests to open new programs and will recommend closings if a program is not educating graduates who can pass the licensure exam and practice at a safe level.

Each diploma school was accustomed to being reviewed by the OBN in accordance with the rules and regulations set out in the Ohio Revised Code, Chapter 4723-5. These regulations outlined curriculum, faculty qualifications and responsibilities, program policies, program administration, and program evaluation. Each year every school submitted a report which outlined the curriculum, tallied up the class and clinical hours, addressed any changes that were planned, and reviewed the effects of changes made since the last report. OBN also reviewed the results of the state board exam pass rates. If pass rates were not what they should be, the program was required to submit a plan for improvement. Currently, acceptable pass rates are researched and changed to take into account both national and state averages. Only first time takers are counted in the schools' achievement of this standard. In addition to the annual reports, representatives of the Board also visited each program at regular intervals to make sure what was in the report was actually in place. The Board could also visit and investigate any time a complaint was filed.

National League for Nursing (NLN)

The late 1800s saw an increase in higher education programs and an increased focus on quality in education. Regional accreditation evolved and institutional accreditation became more accepted. In 1895, the American Society of Superintendents of Training Schools for Nurses was established in response to the increased need for the nursing profession to ensure that the graduates of each program in the United States were prepared at the proper level.

In 1912, this group was renamed the National League for Nursing Education (NLNE). The first set of national accreditation standards were published in 1917. A program seeking NLNE accreditation would write a report addressing how the standards were being met. An accreditation visit was scheduled and based on the report and findings of the visiting team, the program was granted accreditation for a specified number of years. The important thing about this process is that the visits were conducted by other nurse educators currently working in the same kinds of programs in other states.

In 1952, the NLNE combined with the National Organization for Public Health Nursing and the Association for Collegiate Schools of

Nursing to become the National League for Nursing (NLN). In 1997, changes mandated by the United States Department of Education resulted in the formation of a separate entity concerned only with program accreditation. The resulting corporation was called the National League for Nursing Accrediting Commission (NLNAC); in 2013 it had another name change and is currently known as ACEN, the Accreditation Commission for Education in Nursing.

It is important to note that OBN approval is necessary for graduates to take the licensing examination. ACEN accreditation, while highly prized and desirable, is voluntary in Ohio.

CONTENT TO BE TAUGHT

Need to Know versus Nice to Know versus Nuts to Know

Accreditation standards and state regulations specified that the curriculum be up to date and include the current trends in nursing. This need for currency accounts for the constant, regular review of the courses taught in the program.

"I recall getting together with the entire second level faculty to hammer out course objectives. There were several courses in the second level and we worked to create course objectives that related to the overall threads of the THSN curriculum. We would sit there all day word-smithing those objectives as we had to get them 'just right.' The words used in the objectives were important as the students would be evaluated on whether they had met the course objectives or not."

Susan J. Eisel
Flower Hospital School of Nursing, Class of 1977
Faculty, Toledo Hospital School of Nursing

When one considers the discoveries and advancements in medicine and healthcare and the subsequent changes in the care of patients that have occurred over the last 100 years, it is really startling. All of these changes have impacted what nurses do and what they need to know to do it.

Broken down by decade, major discoveries requiring changes in nursing include:

1900's: discovery of blood typing, electrocardiography, existence of vitamins, diseases caused by the lack of vitamins;

1910's: first laparoscopy performed on a human and the wide use of sulfa drugs during World War I;

1920's: discovery of vitamin D and rickets, Banting and Best discover insulin, epidural anesthesia utilized, Fleming discovers penicillin, electroencephalography developed, and the first vaccines for diphtheria, pertussis, tuberculosis, tetanus;

1930's: insulin shock therapy, first vaccine for yellow fever, pre-fontal lobotomy used to treat mental illness, and electroconvulsive therapy developed;

1940's: first dialysis machine built, disposable catheters developed, first chemotherapeutic drugs developed, defibrillator developed, acetaminophen manufactured, first implantable intraocular lens, and mechanical assistor for anesthesia;

1950's: Salk polio vaccine, cloning, heart lung machine, medical ultrasonography, first kidney transplant, tetracycline, metered dose inhaler, pacemaker, and in vitro fertilization;

1960's: CPR, oral contraceptives, hip replacement, beta blockers, first oral polio vaccine, artificial heart, first human liver transplant, first human lung transplant, Valium, first vaccine for measles, first portable defibrillator installed, first commercial ultrasound, first human pancreas transplant, rubella vaccine, first vaccine for mumps, first human heart transplant, controlled drug delivery, internet, balloon catheter, and cochlear transplant;

1970's: cyclosporine, MRI, CT scans, transdermal patches, insulin pump, laser eye surgery, liposuction, and antiviral drugs;

1980's: first vaccine for hepatitis B, artificial skin, human insulin, surgical robot, DNA fingerprinting, commercially available statins, tissue engineering, intravascular stents, and laser cataract surgery;

1990's: first vaccine for hepatitis A, successful cloning of a sheep, stem cell therapy, and artificial muscle.[1]

It has been estimated that knowledge doubles every 14 to 24 months depending on the complexity of the discipline. Soon this may become every 12 hours with the continued growth of technology.[2] "It is estimated that the doubling time of medical knowledge in 1950 was 50 years; in 1980, 7 years, and in 2010, 3.5 years. In 2020 it is projected to be 0.2 years – just 73 days"[3]

With each of these advances came the need to modify and update what was in the curriculum. Not only did students need to be up-to-date in their studies, but the way they were taught needed to stay current as well. As the century progressed, it was no longer practical or possible to memorize facts. Rather, nursing faculty needed to help students understand the concepts of health, illness and medical treatment as they affect the entire person. This accounts for the constant change and evolution of the nursing program curriculum. New treatment modalities were implemented for existing conditions, new diseases were identified, new medications were developed, and the body of medical and nursing knowledge continued to change. How could graduates be expected to practice in the years after leaving their basic programs? Arguably as important as updating the medical and nursing knowledge base was the need to foster critical thinking and problem solving skills. Students were taught how to use critical thinking skills to continue to

[1] Donahue, P.P., RN, FAAN, *Nursing: The Finest Art: An Illustrated History, Second Edition.* 2nd ed. 1996, St. Louis, Mo: Mosby. 535.

[2] Schilling, D.R. *Knowledge Doubling Every 12 Months, Soon to be Every 12 Hours.* 2014

[3] Densen, P.M. *Challenges and Opportunities Facing Medical Education.* Transactions of the American Clinical and Climatological Association 2010.

adapt to their practice settings as well as how to find new information: in short, how to think like a nurse.

"I remember learning how to 'shake down' a thermometer and practicing to take a blood pressure. We had a stethoscope that divided and had double headset to compare results. We practiced on fellow students. We learned First Aid CPR, how to use a fire extinguisher and how to serve at a 'tea.'"

Nancy R. Swartz
Riverside Hospital School of Nursing, Class of 1959

"I always sat in the front. I had to listen and pay attention. I struggled in pediatrics and my instructor would help me. She would follow me around. One day I asked her 'Am I doing that bad?' 'No you're doing good and I just want to make sure it stays that way.'... Nursing school was tough. It made me think like a nurse. It also made me more disciplined."

Suzanne Mary Alexander Owen
St. Vincent Hospital School of Nursing, Class of 1974

Today, the Ohio Board of Nursing does not dictate what courses must be offered, but instead lists in the rules that govern nursing education programs the general topics that must be included in the curriculum, as either a course or part of a course. These include: problem solving, communication, documentation, teaching and learning, safety, leadership, legal and ethical issues, infection control, psychosocial and physiologic care, comfort, pharmacology, anatomy and physiology, chemistry, biology, physics, nutrition, and mathematics. This approach has allowed programs latitude in planning and delivering their respective curricula.

Each program had many similarities and some differences in how courses were sequenced. Most schools started with courses in basic nursing and followed with specialty courses in the second and third levels. Which courses were offered first, second, and so on depended many times on scheduling and clinical availability. Complexity of care and increased responsibility for managing care also played a part in design of the curriculum.

"In 1974-75, we were preparing for a major curriculum overhaul and reshuffling of courses at both second and third levels. A Nursing Management course as the last course that all students would take (at the same time) before graduation was to be added. This course was the first of its kind. As one of a very small number of faculty responsible for the development of this course, I remember on one hand the excitement of developing something brand new, but on the other hand feeling the enormity of the responsibility."

Judy Harris Szor
Toledo Hospital School of Nursing, Class of 1966
Faculty, Toledo Hospital School of Nursing

"The year that our curriculum was reviewed and updated was one of the highlights of my career in nursing education. I learned so much. The faculty worked together to organize the curriculum around seven concepts that we believed were important for all beginning professional nurses. I remember them to this day. We called them the seven threads: Knowledge, Nursing Process, Technical Skills, Teaching-Learning, Communication, Community and Professionalism.

Beth Heinzeroth White
St. Vincent Hospital School of Nursing, Class of 1973
Faculty, Toledo Hospital School of Nursing

Physical Science, Social Science, Philosophy, and University Credits

Physical science courses provided a strong base to understand the rationale underlying nursing actions while the social sciences helped the student understand human behavior. Educators recognized the need to add both physical and social sciences to the plan of study. Each program required a different set of courses, but which usually included the following physical science courses: Anatomy and Physiology, Chemistry, and Microbiology. Many also required one or more of the following Social Sciences: Psychology, Sociology, Abnormal Psychology, and Human Sexuality. The ethical considerations in healthcare were also explored in Medical Ethics, a course taught in the Philosophy or Religion Departments of the local colleges.

"Our science classes were taught by doctors over at Scott High School. We worked nights and then attended class. We had to work a lot on the floors, and then we had class."

Mary Findlay Root
Robinwood Hospital School of Nursing, Class of 1943

As more courses in the physical and social sciences were added to the curriculum of each local school, programs contracted with local colleges and universities to have their students attend.

A pair of nursing students use microscopes in their microbiology lab in 1957. (Photo courtesy of Mercy College of Ohio archives)

Travel to universities for basic courses became part of the students' days in the early-1900s. Students of the Toledo Hospital School of Nursing began taking their science courses at the University of Toledo in the mid-1930s, and the *Toledo Blade* documented in June 1943 that five area diploma nursing programs were beginning a new cooperative program with the University of Toledo. A University of Toledo bulletin clarified this to be a centralized program in nursing education for the U.S. Cadet Nurse Corps. Courses included were anatomy and physiology for nurses, microbiology for nurses, chemistry for nurses, college composition, and psychology for nurses. The schools of nursing included were Flower Hospital, Robinwood Hospital, the Toledo Hospital, Women's and Children's Hospital, and the Toledo State Hospital. Most schools continued this affiliation with the University after the Cadet Nurse Corps program ended in 1948 as the credits from university courses would transfer. This was very beneficial for any students wanting to later pursue a baccalaureate degree.

Mercy Hospital School of Nursing students took physical, biological, and social sciences at DeSales College from 1938 to 1942. In 1955 they began a 20 year relationship with Mary Manse College initially for chemistry and microbiology. St. Vincent Hospital School of Nursing started its affiliation with Mary Manse College for science courses in 1950s. When Mary Manse College closed in 1975, St. Vincent Hospital School of Nursing students transferred to Lourdes College in Sylvania. Maumee Valley Hospital student nurses also took their science courses at Mary Manse College. According to E. Wanda Quay, who served as director of Riverside Hospital School of Nursing in the late 1950s and early 1960s, the basic science courses were taught at the school of nursing. The retirement of the basic sciences instructor brought about a relationship with the University of Toledo for perhaps two years before the school of nursing closed.

De Sales College was located in the Vistula area of Toledo on the corner of Superior and Walnut in the former St. John's College building. The college was run by the Jesuit order and most of the faculty were priests and nuns. The college was open from 1936 to 1942 and eventually merged with the Toledo Teachers College.[4] The original college building has since been torn down, but one of the other buildings, the Pomeroy House, used as part of the college survives and currently operates as a bed and breakfast.

Lourdes University is located in Sylvania. Lourdes Junior College was founded in 1958 and was primarily used for the education of the Sisters of St. Francis. Lay women were first admitted to the Junior

[4]Batesel, P. *Lost Colleges*. 2010

A 1972 view of the former St. John's College building, also known as the Theodore B. Casey house and Pomeroy Hall, in the 800 block of Huron Street in the Vistula Historic District of Toledo. (Photo courtesy the Toledo-Lucas County Public Library, Images In Time).

College in 1969. In 1973 it was incorporated as Lourdes College. In 1975, educational opportunities were extended to students from the St. Vincent Hospital School of Nursing. In 1981, the college received approval from its board to move to a four year college. In 2011, Lourdes College became Lourdes University.

Mary Manse College was located in Toledo's Old West End historic neighborhood. It operated from 1922 to 1975. Mary Manse, run by the Ursuline order of nuns, was opened as a women's college and remained that way until 1971 when it became co-educational. Mary Manse was hit with difficulties during the recession of 1971 and was forced to declare bankruptcy and eventually closed in 1975.

The former convent for the Ursuline Order of the Sacred Heart, this complex later housed Mary Manse College and St. Ursula Academy. A registered historical site, the facility, in the 2400 block of Collingwood Boulevard, is currently home to the Collingwood Arts Center. Photo c. 1945. (Photo courtesy the Toledo-Lucas County Public Library, Images In Time).

"Classes were good but tough. We spent every Monday, Wednesday, and Friday at Mary Manse College for Chemistry and Anatomy. I remember our first oral quiz naming every bone in the body."

Betty Spencer Lemon
St. Vincent Hospital School of Nursing, Class of 1958

"I had no idea what to expect of classes. I had to adjust to not only the college courses at Mary Manse but that I would be responsible for patients' lives. My Big Sis helped a lot; helped me learn the ropes. Classes were different from high school. They were very intense. I think about half of our class was failing chemistry at Mary Manse at Christmas break. I wasn't failing but I remember not wanting to go back."

Norma Provencher Lake
St. Vincent Hospital School of Nursing, Class of 1974

University of Toledo's former Community and Technical College, at the Scott Park campus, housed the university's two-year associate degree programs. Mercy School of Nursing students attended classes here after Mary Manse College closed. Toledo Hospital School of Nursing students attended the main campus of the University of Toledo on Bancroft Street.

"I did not expect to take class at the university when I entered; this was a surprise, those prerequisites at University of Toledo. We got 12 college credits our first year. As a group we would leave out of Croxton House dorm and walk through Ottawa Park woods to the University of Toledo on Bancroft Street. I didn't appreciate the college credits then but did later when I went back to school to get my BSN. But I believe those science courses weeded out half of our class, the freshman. They were tough."

Alene Duerk
Toledo Hospital School of Nursing, Class of 1941

"We had full day classes and large numbers in them. We traveled to the University of Toledo Community and Technical College for science courses."

Carol Annesser
Mercy School of Nursing, Class of 1980

FACULTY

"I remember having students on the oncology unit for clinicals. I was checking how prepared they were to give patient care; asking questions, looking at their paperwork. One student in particular did not seem to know the meds and was not prepared with a plan of care. I told her that she had to look certain things up before I could allow her to give patient care. We were always concerned about patient safety. She seemed to understand what I expected and I directed her to come back and find me

Students at Mercy Hospital School of Nursing listen to a lecture presented by Sister Patricia Ann Dalke RN, MSN. (Photo courtesy the Mercy College of Ohio Archives).

when she thought she was ready. She said, 'Yes, Mrs. Bitch.' I assumed she meant to say, 'Yes, Mrs. Beach.' What a Freudian slip that was! Anyhow, it was so outrageous I had to laugh and she was very embarrassed."

Patricia Ringos Beach
St. Elizabeth Hospital School of Nursing, Class of 1976
Faculty, Toledo Hospital School of Nursing

Looking at school of nursing faculty lists from the 1940s, 1950s, and 1960s, there were few individuals with academic degrees beyond their nursing degrees. The 1970s and 1980s saw changes in accreditation standards that required advanced degrees and more faculty members enrolled at local college and universities. Many had to relocate because of the few programs offering higher degree programs in nursing.

Mary Manse College offered a bachelor's degree in nursing education to meet this new demand. In 1970, a Bachelor of Science

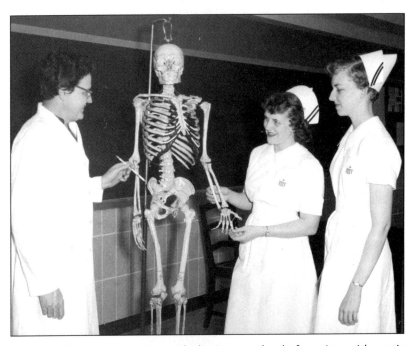

Mrs. Hazel Else, an instructor with the Mercy school of nursing, with a pair of nursing students in the 1950s. (Photo courtesy Mercy College of Ohio archives)

in Nursing program was established at what was then the Medical College of Ohio, and was a joint program of the University of Toledo, Bowling Green State University, and Medical College of Ohio. Today, the University of Toledo, Lourdes University, and Mercy College of Ohio offer baccalaureate degrees in nursing as well as graduate degrees in a variety of nursing specialties. Currently the State Board of Ohio requires that diploma school faculty have a bachelor's degree in nursing as well as a master's degree, preferably in nursing.

"I wanted to earn a Master of Science in Nursing. It seemed that if I was going to continue teaching in a school of nursing, I needed more in-depth nursing knowledge. There was no MSN program in the Toledo area. I had to take a leave from my job and move out of town to accomplish this goal."

Beth Heinzeroth White
St. Vincent Hospital School of Nursing, Class of 1973
Faculty, Toledo Hospital School of Nursing

"I started at Toledo Hospital School of Nursing in spring of 1981 and was very nervous. I felt I was a good floor nurse, but that did not always translate into being an effective teacher. The best opportunity I had at Toledo Hospital School of Nursing was enrolling in a week-long crash course in Ann Arbor. The focus was all on developing the necessary skills to become an educator. In that week-long intensive course, we practiced writing objectives and lesson plans. We also learned about curriculum planning, writing test questions, analyzing test questions, creating course evaluations, and many other topics. By the time I was done I felt I had a solid understanding of at least where to start. There were also many great faculty mentors who helped bring me along and increase my ability to be nurse faculty."

Susan J. Eisel
Flower Hospital School of Nursing, Class of 1977
Faculty, Toledo Hospital School of Nursing

"Well, I had worked in a couple of different intensive care units in
both Youngstown and Columbus, but when we moved to Toledo, I applied
for a faculty position at Toledo Hospital School of Nursing. When I got it
I was thrilled! I guess I thought if I was a good nurse, I would be a good
teacher of nurses."

Patricia Ringos Beach
St. Elizabeth Hospital School of Nursing, Class of 1976
Faculty, Toledo Hospital School of Nursing

In the early years of the Toledo programs, head nurses and supervisors in the hospital taught content in the nursing programs according to specialty. Schools recruited the brightest and the best of their graduates. In the area Catholic schools, nurse nuns of the sponsoring order were often members of the faculty. Hospital physicians also presented on their respective specialties.

"My first classroom responsibility as a faculty member was to teach
and then supervise the lab for senior students on the starting of IVs. The
students practiced on each other in those days (1972) and sometimes on
the instructor. After the class my mentor, Margie Place, asked me how
it went. I replied, 'It was fun, but I could have used more time.' She said
'you're hooked.'"

Judy Harris Szor
Toledo Hospital School of Nursing, Class of 1966
Faculty, Toledo Hospital School of Nursing

"I started teaching Pediatric Nursing right after receiving my Bachelor
of Science in Nursing degree. I had no idea how to develop a lecture and
teach a class. My first class was a two-hour presentation on the growth
and development of infants. The content was a review of three major
developmental theorists and infant nutrition. The age span was newborn
to 12 months of age. I finished in 15 minutes. When I looked up from my

*notes, the class had put down their pens and was just staring at me. My
mentor said 'Let's talk about pacing content.'"*

Beth Heinzeroth White
*St. Vincent Hospital School of Nursing, Class of 1973
Faculty, Toledo Hospital School of Nursing*

*"One of the ways that I was mentored in my new faculty position was
to follow one of the more experienced faculty members as she conducted
her clinical day with students. I saw how she questioned each student in-
depth about their understanding of their patient's diagnoses, lab values,
and other subjects pertinent to their patient care. I thought to myself, 'Boy,
I cannot even answer these questions.' I did a tremendous amount of
studying day and night for those first two years."*

Susan J. Eisel
*Flower Hospital School of Nursing, Class of 1977
Faculty, Toledo Hospital School of Nursing*

*"My first assignment was to teach freshmen nursing students about
pain. I thought, 'I've got this. No one will have ever taught pain better.' I
read all I could, I wrote out notes and handouts. I prepared transparencies
for the overhead projector (no PowerPoint in those days) and had
handouts for the students. I explained pain and pain management
in such detail, including the Gate Theory, that there could have been
no question that the subject was covered. At the end of the course, the
student evaluations came in. These were anonymous. And I remember
my evaluations being terrible. Anyhow, after I got over my hurt feelings,
I read them carefully, especially the comments. Some students were very
thoughtful and constructive. They talked about how I read my notes, how
it was too mechanical. It helped me make changes to my lecture style and I
think improve my style. At least my evaluations were better after that."*

Patricia Ringos Beach
*St. Elizabeth Hospital School of Nursing, Class of 1976
Faculty, Toledo Hospital School of Nursing*

There was cooperation among the Toledo diploma schools of nursing through the Diploma Council. E. Wanda Quay, director of Maumee Valley Hospital School of Nursing and Riverside Hospital School of Nursing, was instrumental in starting this group as a way for schools to work together and bring in speakers who were beneficial to all to enrich faculty teaching. This meant that more faculty members were able to attend presentations rather than sending one or two members to conferences. It was cost effective and provided a networking opportunity for faculty in the area.

"I remember running into Sister Patricia Ann Dalke at one of these meetings when I was a faculty member at Toledo Hospital School of Nursing. Sister Pat was the Director at Mercy Hospital School of Nursing at the time. She hugged me and told me she was glad to see me and heard that I had been doing a good job at Toledo Hospital School of Nursing. She then whispered in my ear 'A lot of maturing must have taken place.' I guess I must have tried her patience a few times as a student of hers."

Maria Nowicki
Mercy School of Nursing, Class of 1970
Faculty, Toledo Hospital School of Nursing 1980-1985
Faculty, Mercy School of Nursing 1986-1992

TESTING AND GRADING

Where there is education and schooling, there is testing. Classroom testing was continuously improved to measure more than just memorization of facts. Knowing that procedures, medications, and treatments were constantly changing, faculty developed test questions that assessed students' ability to problem solve. As the licensing exam evolved to address patient needs rather than the medical model, faculty were challenged to develop questions that required nursing judgment calls.

Instead of questions asking about lab values or symptoms of a disease, students were given lab values and presenting symptoms and asked what their first—or priority nursing—action would be. Case studies were used. From a list of five patients, students could be asked to evaluate each one and decide who to see first, whose care could be delegated, and what nursing interventions were appropriate.

Standardized tests given at the end of courses were another way to measure program effectiveness of content presentation and student understanding. NLN tests (created and sold by the National League for Nursing) were most common and covered nursing course content: Fundamentals of Nursing, Pediatrics, Obstetrics, Medical Nursing, Surgical Nursing, and Psychiatric Nursing. These tests helped the school compare its student performance to like schools. Student performance on these tests also offered faculty a means to evaluate and update the curriculum.

Students had to achieve a "C" or better in all required nursing courses to advance through the program. If a student missed the cut off by even a tenth of a point they failed the course. Many of the schools had strict progression policies. In some programs, one nursing course failure resulted in dismissal from the program. Others allowed one course repeat and subsequent failures resulted in dismissal from the program.

Many diploma schools had grading scales for nursing courses that were much higher than those used in the college and university courses. For example, a cut off of 79 percent or 80 percent rather than 75 percent equaled a C. There was not a standard scale used at all schools, but a program had to prove to the Ohio Board of Nursing and NLN that it adhered to the published scale, which explained the strict adherence to the grading policy.

Toledo Hospital School of Nursing Croxton House Library was always a popular place for quiet study for students. (Photo courtesy of the Promedica Toledo Hospital Archives)

"I always told my students 'I will never correct you in front of a patient, if you hear me start to sing, excuse yourself from the patient's bedside and we'll go out of the room and talk about what was going wrong.' Students measured a successful rotation by my never having to sing at them."

Maria Nowicki
Mercy School of Nursing, Class of 1970
Faculty, Toledo Hospital School of Nursing 1980-1985
Faculty, Mercy Hospital School of Nursing 1986-1992

In the early twentieth century, it was not unusual for a student to spend 80 or more hours each week in classroom and clinical time. Even in the 1980s and 1990s, students were typically logging 26 hours each week in class and clinical time. When lab practice time, clinical preparation time, and of course study time were added, students could realistically spend 50 to 60 hours each week learning to be a nurse.

In Catholic hospital schools, the students were also assigned communion calls on a rotating basis. They were expected to be at Mass at 6 a.m. and accompany the priest while he distributed communion to patients. A student so assigned was expected to be in full uniform and carried a candle and rang a bell to alert the floor staff that the priest was on the floor.

Learning to be a nurse in a diploma school was a difficult program of study. It was a time of amazing experiences, daily surprises and wonderful rewards. And it was worth all the work and effort.

Chapter 5
Healing...Like a Nurse

*"For the sick it is important to have the best." – **Florence Nightingale***

Many nurses, those who are diploma school graduates and those who are not, understand clinicals were the hallmark of diploma nursing education. Clinicals were the real-world setting where students learned to care for patients. However, "clinicals" is not technically even a real word. Spell-check will tag it as misspelled every time. Merriam-Webster proclaims that clinical is an adjective that does not have a plural conjugate. It defines clinical as "relating to or based on work done with real patients; of or relating to the medical treatment that is given to patients in hospitals, clinics, etc.; requiring treatment as a medical problem; of or relating to a place where medical treatment is given; of or relating to a clinic."

Diploma student nurses were immersed in the practice of caring for patients. When the word "clinicals" is used in nursing education, it means practice caring for patients. This is where theory meets practice; this is hands on care, caring for real people with real health problems. It is where the rubber meets the road.

Nurses have always known that clinicals are the real world. Taking care of patients required the student nurse to adapt to dramatic changes in thinking, speaking, and behaving. Diploma school student nurses learned early that caring for patients involved complicated and voluminous amounts of information. Competent patient care required understanding normal physical and emotional health parameters, knowledge of disease processes and medical treatment, thoughtful consideration of the patients' responses to disease, and technical skill.

Student nurses also had to learn a "new" language, one full of abbreviations and acronyms. In the earliest of years, students who knew some Latin had a bit of an edge, as many of these abbreviations are rooted in the classic language. The amount of information communicated between colleagues required nurses to speak in language short cuts that all understood. Student nurses needed to learn to translate such sentences as:

"Check Mr. Jones' glucose a.c. and h.s., and cover him PRN." Translation: Mr. Jones is a diabetic patient who needs to have his blood sugar checked before every meal and at bedtime. If his blood sugar is above recommended levels, he is to receive regular insulin at a dose that corresponds to his blood sugar level.

Kathleen Roper, St. Vincent Hospital School of Nursing Class of 1984, draws medication into a syringe from a multi-use vial. She is standing at a medication cart, which contains the prescribed medications for each patient on her floor. (Photo courtesy of the Mercy Health/St. Vincent archives)

"Mrs. Smith's afib responded to cardioversion, on doftilide, has antiems." Translation: Mrs. Smith has a heart rhythm problem called atrial fibrillation, where the upper chambers of her heart beat too often and irregularly, and it can cause heart attacks and strokes. Mrs. Smith had her heart rhythm treated with an electrical shock called cardioversion and treated with a medication called doftilide to keep the heart in the correct rhythm. She is also wearing elastic hose to support the veins and arteries in her legs so she does not develop a blood clot that might lead to a heart attack or stroke.

Besides the language, other new skills required practice to improve and become expert, for example, taking a blood pressure, changing a wound dressing, or relieving pain. Clinicals were the cornerstone and distinction upon which diploma nursing was built. Because of clinicals, diploma schools graduated experienced nurses with skill in patient care. Students' experiences with clinicals were difficult, yet rewarding and memorable. Clinicals were an all-encompassing, life-changing commitment; each student was expected to give their all.

"I was sure I couldn't be a nurse. I fainted during my admission lab work the first week of school. When I gave my first shot, I kind of got over it."

Elaine Studer Hetherwick
Maumee Valley Hospital School of Nursing, Class of 1966

"I remember clinicals as very enjoyable. Safety was a big issue. For example with call lights, side rails, getting patients to bedside commodes. And we had check-off forms for clinical performance."

Cassandra Willey Zak
Toledo Hospital School of Nursing, Class of 1972

"I loved having my own patient and reading up on them and their care the night before clinicals. At that point they became more than a diagnosis or room number, they became real people."

Kaye Lani Rae Rafko Wilson
St. Vincent Hospital School of Nursing, Class of 1985

CLINICALS AS HALLMARK OF DIPLOMA EDUCATION

The correlation of classroom theory to clinical experience was a distinguishing hallmark of diploma school nursing education.

When the Bachelor of Science in Nursing (BSN) degree became widely available and nursing practice and education leaders were calling for the BSN as the entry into professional nursing practice, fewer clinical hours were required. Subsequently, graduates often required additional clinical experience in their first hospital positions to function competently.

Despite the move to BSN programs, diploma nursing survived. It survived in large part because of the rallying cry from diploma school faculty and practicing nurses, "What about clinicals?" "We cannot lose clinicals," and "Clinicals are valuable." Among other things, hospitals valued diploma graduates because they were ready to begin taking care of patients the day they graduated.

Clinicals changed over the 100 years diploma schools operated in Toledo. They progressed as the hospital environment and education progressed. Clinicals evolved from just being a way to staff hospitals—from "do as I do"—to being essential for students to integrate theory into practice as they learned to develop critical thinking skills that would prepare them for lifelong learning. Clinicals were planned with other curricula considerations such as content specificity, credit hours, and required outcomes for graduation. The value of clinicals was weighed against scheduling and credits as a student's time was evaluated by an academic model rather than the needs of the hospital. A balance of classroom and clinical practice workload continue today in all nursing programs.

One unique aspect of clinicals in diploma education in the first few decades of the twentieth century was assigning students to private duty cases or "specials." The hospital, not the student, was paid for this work. Although some programs like the Toledo Hospital School of Nursing did allow the student who did "specializing" in a private residence to receive a portion of the fee, many others had all wages come to the hospital. [1] When graduates were working primarily as private duty nurses there may have been some justification for this type of experience. However,

[1] Weiser, PJ, A Legacy of Caring: A History of the Toledo Hospital School of Nursing. (Toledo, OH: Wayne Graphics, 1988), 17.

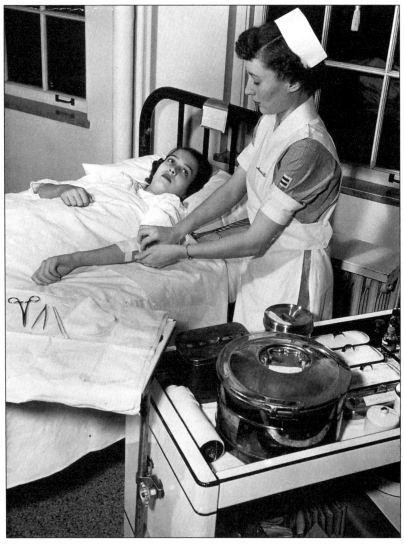

Here a student is changing a dressing at the bedside. Her equipment included a well-stocked cart of supplies. Clinicals emphasized always ready, prepared, and organized. (Photo courtesy of Promedica Toledo Hospital Archives)

in the first quarter of the twentieth century hospitals were growing and nursing positions in specialty areas like public health, administration, teaching, office nursing, industrial nursing, and pediatrics were in demand. Eventually this practice of hiring out student nurses for private duty assignments was ended by nurse educators who viewed it as exploitive.[2][3]

Clinical experience began in the learning laboratory. This was often called the nursing arts or nursing skills laboratory. Experiences here varied from practicing skills on other student nurses, to role-playing actors in certain scenarios, to practicing skills on mannequins that became increasingly technologically advanced.

Lena Smith Yoder, Flower Hospital School of Nursing class of 1916, remembered that "all students spent some time in the lab, usually two weeks. We washed glassware, learned to do red and white blood counts, urinalysis, and to test urine for sugar. This test was done by taking a special little 'glass' into which was poured a measured amount of urine. A little piece of yeast cake was dropped in, the glass was covered and after waiting a designated amount of time you observed how much gas was made. It did not do much except show there was sugar in the urine; at that time there was no way to treat diabetes and we knew the patient would soon die. Insulin was not discovered until 1921."[4]

The importance of procedure and detail was stressed to students throughout their clinicals. The impression was long-lasting. In her unpublished memoir, Mary Ann Shea Arquette, St. Vincent School of Nursing class of 1942, recounts:

> "Routinely, each patient was to have a temperature reading
> in early morning right after day shift came on duty and again in
> late afternoon. The procedure was as follows: The nurse took the
> thermometer out of a tube, wiped it with a cotton ball, checked
> the level of mercury in thermometer, shook the thermometer

[2]Rodabaugh JH & Rodabaugh MJ, Nursing in Ohio: A History. (Columbus, OH: The Ohio State Nurses' Association, 1951), 129, 136-137.

[3]Kalisch, PA & Kalisch, BJ, American Nursing: A History. (Philadelphia: Lippincott Williams & Wilkins, 2004). 115-116.

[4]Author unknown, Flower Hospital School of Nursing 1909-1977,8.

with a snapping wrist action until the mercury was level with 96 (degrees) or below, insert the thermometer under the patient's tongue for at least one minute while taking the patient's pulse at the wrist (radial pulse), removing the thermometer, checking the reading, wiping the thermometer with a cotton ball, and placing it back in the test tube. She had also observed the rate of the patient's respiration. All three measurements were recorded in her pocket notebook to be entered on the patient's chart when she had finished with the assignment...any higher than expected numbers were reported to the Head Nurse promptly.[5]

By the 1950s, clinicals focused on experiences that graduates would need to provide patient care and were correlated with classroom content. The *St. Luke's Hospital School of Nursing Bulletin 1952-1954* described what students could expect each year of their education.

1. First or Freshman Year...During the second semester intensive instruction is given in the principles and practice of nursing, and includes class, study, laboratory practice periods, and supervised practice in patient care at the hospital.
2. Second or Junior Year...The second year stresses the principles of nursing care of patients with medical-surgical conditions, medical-surgical specialties, and obstetrics. Students are assigned to the various clinical services for correlating experiences and to the diet kitchen and operating rooms for specialized experience.
3. Third or Senior Year...This year is devoted to the affiliation courses in pediatric and psychiatric nursing when instruction and experience are given in these

[5]Arquette, M.A.S, My Life So Far. (Unpublished, c. 2007-2010), 18.

clinical areas. The remainder of the year provides for advance medical-surgical experience and for consideration of the problems the nurses may meet after graduation.

Student experience evolved with technology but always emphasized care of the patient, cleanliness of environment, and efficiency. These experiences grew from performing physical tasks and procedures to developing a holistic view of the patient's response to illness and treatment. Evidence of critical thinking and problem solving abilities in patient care situations was increasingly emphasized in the latter years of diploma education.

"Clinicals helped put theory and practice together. I will never forget the smell of pseudomonas in a leg wound. I also remember clearly understanding pyloric stenosis after feeding a baby who then had projectile vomit. It all made sense. The theory clicked. It was a light bulb moment for me."

Linda Graver Lucas
Toledo Hospital School of Nursing, Class of 1984

"Days were long. We started with clinical from 7 a.m. to 10 a.m. and had to get all the care done for our three patients; then we would go to class; then back to the hospital to help patients with dinner and get ready for the night; then mandatory study time until 10 p.m."

Alice Miller
Toledo Hospital School of Nursing, Class of 1941

"The number of patients we cared for helped me feel like I was a nurse. It made me believe in myself, that I could learn how to make a difference in the lives of patients."

Norma Provencher Lake
St. Vincent Hospital School of Nursing, Class of 1974

"We had a rotation through Central Supply where we scrubbed the metal bed pans to re-use. Had some sort of steam apparatus to sterilize them. We washed rubber gloves, flipped them at the wrist to check them for holes, wrapped them in paper packages and autoclaved them. Would force alcohol through needles and check them for 'spurs'. Put them in covered metal trays and autoclaved them. Syringes were cleaned the same way. They were glass and reused ... When we worked in the newborn nursery we had to wear hair nets. Don't dare get caught without one, because the OB Clinical Instructor was a fanatic about them. We had to wash with soap and water between changing a diaper or handling a newborn each time. There were no disposable gloves or hand sanitizer."

Nancy R. Swartz
Riverside Hospital School of
Nursing, Class of 1959

Standing on the steps of the nurses' residence at Lucas County Hospital School of Nursing, (later Maumee Valley Hospital School of Nursing) a beaming Virginia Williams Whitmore, Class of 1943, prepares to leave for clinicals in her crisp uniform. (Photo courtesy of the Whitmore family).

"As a faculty member, I will never forget how seriously we took our responsibility to assure the clinical competence of our graduates. At the end of every course, all instructors in that course met together to

review the clinical performance of each student throughout the term. Sometimes many hours were spent in reviews in determining if students had met the objectives or not. It was a decision that weighed heavily on everyone."

Judy Harris Szor
Toledo Hospital School of Nursing, Class of 1966
Faculty, Toledo Hospital School of Nursing

"I remember the lab for the Fundamentals of Nursing, taking temps, making beds, learning comfort measures. I remember S. M. at Toledo Hospital. She was very tough, but I remember her saying she wanted us to know the correct techniques. That was to insure in actual nursing we would make good choices, when circumstances changed our plans for care. She had very high standards and set a powerful example. She was not a friend but a true teacher."

Karen Steinmetz Christian
Maumee Valley Hospital School of Nursing, Class of 1968

"Back in the 70s we gave a lot of IM (intramuscular) injections. IVs (intravenous) were rare. If you had a patient with an IV you regulated it by counting drops."

Janice Smith Cook
Flower Hospital School of Nursing, Class of 1976

"I remember a little awkwardness in the learning lab when we were supposed to do a bed bath on another student. There were not enough male students for me to have a male partner. Annie, an older student, was my partner. It worked out ok."

Jeff Lycan
Toledo Hospital School of Nursing, Class of 1984

DIPLOMA STUDENT NURSES AS LABOR FORCE FOR HOSPITALS

In the early part of the twentieth century, clinicals were almost the students' entire world. The evolution of diploma schools of nursing parallels the development of hospitals. As hospitals increased in size and number, so did diploma schools. Hospital expansion also required more personnel, and student nurses were necessary to staff the growing hospitals. That is how a hospital expected to "meet its budget." A hospital's need to provide patient care through students' clinical work sometimes overshadowed the educational needs of students. In these years when students were assigned to staff hospitals, often these assignments were repetitive. Practice made perfect but did not allow for a wide range of varied experience.

For diploma nursing students the real world of clinicals often clashed with their romanticized visions of nursing. The 1960 St. Vincent School of Nursing yearbook, *The Vincentine*, passionately extols, "The key to nursing is love. Through love for patients, the nurse is able to

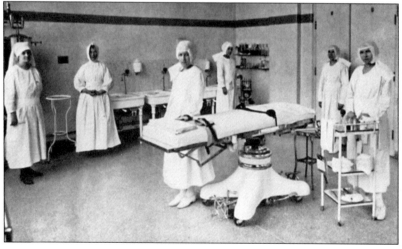

This operating room early in the twentieth century shows cleanliness and preparedness but there is not a glove in sight. Antibiotics and asepsis were little known at this time. (Photo courtesy of Mercy Health/St. Vincent archives)

159

enjoy the satisfaction of knowing she is living her life in the best possible way—a life of dedication to others. In the nurse there is an innate desire to console and help others. Nursing fulfills this need; it is her key to the future. In accordance with this desire, the nurse strives to be gentle and loving when she cares for her patients."[6]

In reality, clinicals were hard work. Love and dedication were not idealized concepts in clinicals, but grounded in the best practices of nursing. Through intense and frequent patient care experiences a student's skills were honed. Clinicals had stringent evaluation criteria and nothing but the most consistent standard of excellence was acceptable.

The conviction that diploma nursing education was good for the hospital and the nurse was strongly held. Dr. Thomas Hales, administrator at Albany Hospital in New York, stated that hospital and school must work together for success and a balanced budget.[7] The steps to achieve this were:

1. Hospital and school must agree that their objective is to turn out a competent bedside nurse.
2. Hospital and school must believe in the 'apprenticeship' philosophy of nurse education-that the student 'learns by doing,' and that she cannot learn nursing skills by spending most of her time in the classroom and laboratory.
3. They must agree that 'repetitive practice' is valuable in the training of a student nurse because every patient presents a different challenge.
4. They must be willing to cut to the minimum the assignment

---

[6]*The Vincentine* (1960), 51.

[7]Kalisch, PA & Kalisch, BJ, American Nursing: A History. (Philadelphia: Lippincott Williams & Wilkins, 2004), 389.

of students that take them away from the service areas where patient care is provided.

5. Vacation, holiday, and sick leave policies must be kept on a realistic basis. They cannot follow college campus patterns without bankrupting the school.

6. A work week of no less than 40 hours (preferable 44 hours) of combined classroom and ward experience is essential for the sound financial operation of the school.

7. A reasonable and fair evaluation of student services must be developed.

8. Strict accounting must be kept of the student's time on the wards when she is rendering the services to patients that justify the hospital in compensating for these services.

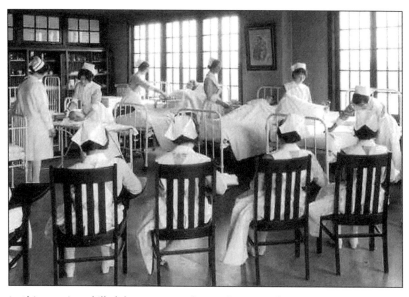

In this nursing skills laboratory students observe others as mannequins are used instead of real patients. After skills were demonstrated satisfactorily or "checked off" they would be performed on patients in the hospital setting. (Photo courtesy of Mercy Health/St. Vincent archives)

Most schools began the relationship between students and hospital work with a probation period. Incoming freshmen were on a probationary or "probie" status. In the early years of diploma education, probie time was used to have the students do the work of a chambermaid. It did not resemble nursing skills but included dusting, scrubbing, and washing dishes.[8] Later during these few weeks, usually no longer than one term, students were taught and supervised in patient care skills. Often this was in a laboratory or nursing arts skill setting. Once this period was ended, they were assigned to work on the hospital floors or wards. Although the probation period persisted in many schools, the work evolved over time to be more professionally directed and less like housekeeping.

Once in the hospital setting, students did all the work that was expected of a graduate nurse. Through the 1950s, student nurses were in charge of the hospital patient care areas. For example, there may be a registered nurse supervisor for the entire hospital during the night, but each ward was staffed by students.

In a personal memoir, *Flower Hospital School of Nursing 1909-1977*, Emma Huber Hawkins, class of 1912, is quoted as remembering that, "… surgery was carrying pails and pails of water to fill the autoclave every morning. The water had to be carried from the doctor's scrub room down the hall, then she climbed up on a chair and poured the water through a funnel into the top of the autoclave. Approximately five pails of water were needed to fill it so the steam could be turned on and sterilizing begun for the day. At the end of the day, after seven o'clock, all the water was drained off into the pails, carried back down the hall and poured out."[9]

Later, the student's educational needs were considered and clinical hours to staff hospitals decreased. During this period the emphasis was still on development of skills but clinicals were assigned according to

[8] Kalisch, P.A. & Kalisch, B.J., American Nursing: A History. (Philadelphia: Lippincott Williams & Wilkins, 2004), 116.

[9] Hawkins, E.H., Flower Hospital School of Nursing 1909-1977, 7.

162

content taught in the classroom. Course materials were developed in conjunction with clinical assignments to enhance learning. Clinical instructors, rather than the hospital nursing staff, were responsible for student performance. Students received a grade for classroom work and testing and a grade for clinicals, often pass/fail or satisfactory/ unsatisfactory. The grade for clinicals was as important as the classroom grade. Then as now, each had to be passing for the student to advance.

Student experiences cannot be considered out of the societal context. Many remember treating doctors not only respectfully but unquestioningly to acknowledge their more powerful status. Separate charting areas for doctors and nurses and student nurses were common. "Speaking only if spoken to" was another common admonition. Much of this cultural attitude reflected the fact that most doctors were men and most nurses were women. In society, women did not yet have all the rights and privileges as men did, and this carried into the hospital environment and was considered respectful rather than submissive.

Betty Spencer Lemon, St. Vincent Hospital School of Nursing Class of 1958, leaves her dorm room for a night clinical assignment in the hospital. (Photo courtesy of Betty Spencer Lemon).

As professional nursing evolved, its unique contribution to health care was refined as expertise in addressing the patients' responses to illness, physically, psychosocially, and spiritually. In the same way, the skills required of students evolved. For example, in the pediatric nursing courses, a student might be assigned to assess and follow a family over time. The student applied the principles of growth and development and family theory. The student would learn how an ill child affects the family and provide necessary instruction to both parents and child. This was different from the single patient assignments during a hospitalization.

Recognition of nursing as an independent profession furthered the emphasis on collegial relationships with the other healthcare team members including physicians. Clear written and verbal communication skills were required to foster interdisciplinary care. Problem solving and conceptual thinking were skills expected in the clinical setting. Evidence based practice, rather than relying on knowledge based solely on "this is the way it has always been done," or "because I said so," became the expectation. The parallel can easily be drawn between the growth of professional nursing and the development of professional nursing education.

Although it changed througout the years, student nurses played a crucial role in hospital staffing. This was very evident one summer night in 1940.

FIRE!

On July 16, 1940, a three-alarm fire alert was sounded at St. Vincent Hospital. More than 140 patients were moved and saved as a fire swept down from the attic above their ward, known as St. Mary's Hall. Two firemen were treated for smoke related injuries. Reports describe the calm and heroic actions of staff – nurses, interns, orderlies, firemen, policemen – and the hysteria of onlookers and family members. Later investigation determined the cause to be faulty electrical wiring. The fire caused an estimated to be $25,000 in damages.[10] [11]

Part of the story that did not get much publicity was the courage of two freshmen nursing students, both 19 years old, who were in charge of those patients that night on the 7 p.m. to 7 a.m. shift. Mary Ann Shea Arquette, one of these students, recounted the following story many years later:[12]

Sister St. Louis, director of St. Vincent Hospital School of Nursing, had called me into her office on the morning that I was completing the usual six weeks stretch of night duty. She said there was a problem in having another student to take my place (maybe it was sickness – I don't remember). So, instead of leaving to go home on an over-night off, I would now work one more week of this night duty assignment. So Carolyn Crook and I were on duty in the Women's Ward on the third floor of the older part of the hospital on that very hot July night in 1940. We had just completed our first year of studies in our three-year program.

Around 10:30 p.m., the patients in one of the larger ward rooms called to me and pointed out a sort of red glow above the ceiling where there was a small opening beside the metal pole which extended from the ceiling and served as the rod to hold privacy curtains for the patient's bed. All ward rooms were fitted with these rods/curtains. They asked me if I thought there

[10]The *Toledo Blade, 142 Escape St. Vincent's Fire*, July 17, 1940.

[11]The *Toledo Blade, Hospital Fire Highlighted by Heroic Efforts*, July 19, 1940.

[12]Arquette, M.A.S, *My Life So Far*. (Unpublished, c. 2007-2010), 21-23.

was a fire in the attic above the ward room.

Speaking calmly, I said I didn't think so, but I would call the supervisor and have it checked. I did so immediately. Note that I didn't go screaming 'Fire!' Sister came at once and she and one of the orderlies and a passing intern whom she pressed into service, went up the small curved staircase near our utility room. After a few minutes they came down and said all was well…

A few minutes later my patients called me again, their observation was that whatever it was, it was doing it again, and what did I think it was. I had to say that I didn't know, either. We didn't see flames. We didn't smell smoke. I said I'd go right to the phone and call for assistance to investigate. And I did.

Sister Night Nun, supervisor for the whole hospital at night, recognized the urgency in my voice, quiet but urgent. She said, 'I will call the fire department. Stay with the patients.' She did. I did.

I reported to the ladies in their beds that the investigative process had been started and that we would stay in the room with them in the meantime. This had never been covered in our Procedure Book, but we couldn't have handled it better. It had been drilled into us that personnel never panicked … And suddenly there were a lot of people all over the place. The medical interns had been awakened and were part of the crowd, firemen in their special clothing were seemingly all over at once. Stretchers appeared as if by magic for the removal of every one of the patients from the Women's Ward, because, indeed there was a fire in the fourth floor/attic/specimen storage room and before the night was over, the whole middle of the Hospital... was awash with big hoses spurting water all over.

Carolyn and I did our best to salvage the patients' charts. I think we got them all and in reasonably good shape, i.e. readable, even if a little water logged with wrinkly pages as they dried... Every empty bed in the house was pressed into use. Some patients ended up on mattresses on floors, when the stretchers had to be used to transport others. Carolyn and I spent part of the night trying to find where the patients were, so we could match the charts to the patients. Those charts with their doctors' orders regarding treatments, medications, and other important information were essential to patient welfare.

We also had to concern ourselves with the birds. In that era, at the far end of each wing was a solarium. With windows on three sides that often were opened for fresh air, during the day patients were encouraged to enjoy the area. Canary birds were also kept in cages in the solarium. For many patients their singing reminded them of home because canaries were popular in Toledo homes at the time. It was the night nurse's duty to see that the canaries had fresh water, a towel covering their cage for the night, and that the towel was removed between 6 and 7 a.m. All the birds survived the fire.

And then there was the narcotic box. I remember going back into the watery mess of Women's Ward with the narcotic key to open the little wall recess in the chart room and taking out the narcotic box so I could give it to the Night Nun. I was scolded by the firemen in the area who shouted that the dripping ceiling could fall down at any time and I would be a victim. Better that than facing the powers that be without delivering that box, I said. My cap got soaked along with my hair. But I recovered the box and gave it, along with the key, to Sister.

Nothing much was made of how we had comported ourselves during that crisis. Sister St. Louis only gave Carolyn and me a brief nod of commendation, if you could call it that. No accolades; no "well done." I recall feeling that you'd think it was just an ordinary occurrence. But that was the way it was all through our three years at St. Vincent. Nobody was ever in danger of being spoiled by praise. I guess it was a toughening process. We were taught to be careful and caring; to know what we were doing and why. Much was demanded and much given in our three year nursing program. We graduates look back in gratitude. Much was expected and much was rendered.

"Some modern day researchers and writers make it sound like the hospital took advantage of the students. I never felt like that. Yes I worked hard but I got a good education."

Mary Ann Shea Arquette
St. Vincent Hospital School of Nursing, Class of 1942

"We ran the hospital. We were it."

Virginia Williams Whitmore
Lucas County Hospital School of Nursing, Class of 1943

"We were 'probies' and low man on the totem pole. We had to give 'complete baths' and carry heavy bath basins to the farthest room at the end of the hall. I remember watching in a group of about three, how to place a foley catheter. We also learned to give soap suds enemas ... After our probation period we were given more and more responsibility. We worked weekends, rotated shifts, sometimes working a full 8 hours and

then attending classes during the day. I do not recall that there always
was a clinical instructor present."

Nancy R. Swartz
Riverside Hospital School of Nursing, Class of 1959

"Students stood up for doctors, got charts for them, and did not
speak to doctors unless spoken to."

Cassandra Willey Zak
Toledo Hospital School of Nursing, Class of 1972

IN-HOSPITAL EXPERIENCES

For the majority of diploma education, the heart of clinicals was the
hospital experience. Clinicals started early; both early in the educational
process and early in the morning with some extending throughout the
night. Any and all vacation time was assigned by the nursing hierarchy.
In the twentieth century, vacation time was granted based on hospital
staffing needs. Students could not take vacation time together. Later,
vacation time corresponded to the academic calendar. Clinicals could
be assigned on any of the three routine shifts: 7 a.m. to 3 p.m., 3 p.m. to
11 p.m., or 11 p.m. to 7 a.m. Responsibilities varied based on the unit
and the student experience level (freshman, junior, senior).

Duties of the student nurse were not always at the bedside. In the
diet kitchen, students learned how to set up trays and how to prepare
special diets for patients. For example, all postoperative patients started
on a liquid diet and then progressed to soft and semi-soft foods. In the
pharmacy, students filled simple prescriptions under close supervision of
the pharmacist.[13] Later, as primary nursing became a model for nursing
care delivery, a student might follow a pregnant woman throughout her
pregnancy observing and participating in prenatal and postnatal care

---

[13]Weiser, P.J., *A Legacy of Caring: A History of the Toledo Hospital School of Nursing*. (Toledo,
OH: Wayne Graphics, 1988), 17.

Medication administration was a skill that was always taken seriously. Here students carefully prepare medications using medication cards, cups, and trays under the watchful eye of Instructor Mary Lou Foos, Mercy Hospital, Class of 1952. (Photo courtesy of Mercy College of Ohio archives)

visits and teaching in an Obstetrical Nursing course. Another student experience in an end-of-life care facility included assigned time at hospice caring for and observing how the family responded to their dying loved one. Student nurses learned to care not just for a patient; the family's needs were also part of the nursing plan of care.

Clinicals came with clinical instructors; who these instructors were and their qualifications changed as diploma education advanced. Early in the century, physicians would teach the theory and nursing supervisors would be responsible for students in the hospital. But for the majority of diploma nursing education, clinical nursing instructors also taught classroom theory. In the latter half of the diploma education era in Toledo, nursing instructors in all programs were required to have advanced degrees. Initially this was a bachelor's degree, and later a master's degree was required to teach.

By 1968, mandatory licensing for registered nurses was in effect in Ohio and the apprenticeship model was in decline. This required students working in the clinical area to be supervised by a clinical instructor and also required that clinical assignments allow for specific nursing experiences. The increased emphasis on educational value and the decreased emphasis on staffing the hospital often necessitated an increase in tuition.[14] Many students chose to augment both income and skill experience by working as a nurse aide or assistant. School rules sometimes prohibited this employment but usually it was valued as a way to increase patient care competence and allow the students to earn money.

Nurses remember clinicals with both fondness and angst. Part of the angst was the rigorous preparation for clinicals. Many recall going to the assigned hospital unit the day before clinicals to find a patient assignment that had been posted by the instructor. The expectation was for the student to review the chart, develop a care plan with priorities, and know the medications the patient was taking. "Med cards" were part of every diploma student nurse's repertoire. These were often hand-written on a 3 x 5 index card. Many are still in attics, saved for some future unknown purpose, or maybe too much work went into them to throw them away. The mantra that a student had to be "safe" to give care was reflected in the hard work of preparation for clinicals. A student could be sure to be questioned and their preparation papers read by the clinical instructor. The care of a patient was a sacred trust.

Observation skills were an important factor in the clinical area as understanding how a patient responded to an illness or treatment is a nursing essential. Florence Nightingale said, "Pathology teaches the harm that disease has done...nothing more. We know nothing of the principle

[14]Compiled by The St. Vincent Medical Center School of Nursing and Alumni Association Centennial History Committee, *A History of St. Vincent Medical Center School of Nursing 1896-1996*, 13.

of health…nothing but observation and experience will teach us the ways to maintain or to bring back the state of health."[15] Observation not only required preparation on the student's part but also written work to be turned in once clinicals were completed. In a paper written in 1970 by Cassandra Willey Zak, Toledo Hospital School of Nursing class of 1972, she carefully recorded her initial observations of her 66-year-old male patient: "Mr. C. is five foot six inches tall and weighs 162 pounds… has gray-white hair that is neatly combed and parted on the left side.

---

[15]Nightingale, Florence, *Notes on Nursing,* (London: Harrison & Sons, 1859), 74.

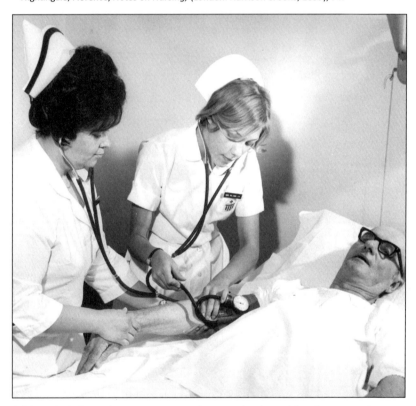

Taking vital signs, (temperature, pulse, respirations, blood pressure) was a clinical skill mastered in Nursing Arts or Fundamentals of Nursing during the first semester. Here, a Mercy School of Nursing student takes a blood pressure with her instructor, Gladys Zyskowski Martinez, listening in using a teaching "double" stethoscope. (Photo courtesy the Mercy College of Ohio archives)

He has a slight receding hairline. His light blue eyes are crinkled, which goes along with his kindly looking face. He has a nice smile and no false teeth." Paperwork and the preparation of medication cards have been simplified and scaled back both to reflect "critical thinking skills and to decrease the emphasis on exact wording," said Luann Schuerman Snyder, faculty member at Owens Community College.

"First memories of clinical experiences were taking vitals on all the patients on the unit between 7 to 8 a.m. and helping patients with baths ... I liked med-surg, OB and Pediatrics. I did not like surgery. Surgery scared me. I was never sure what I was to do. We had to take calls overnight. When you got a call you had to get the key from the switchboard operator and find out what the case was. You went into the dark surgery area, found the lights, and got the surgery equipment set up. The night supervisor then came up and circulated for the surgery."

Barbara Halpin Adamczak
St. Vincent Hospital School of Nursing, Class of 1958

"My patient didn't tell me he had a prosthetic leg. He had undone the clamps and it came off when I was taking off his shoes. I fell right on the floor."

Mary Ann Shea Arquette
St. Vincent Hospital School of Nursing, Class of 1942

"I took care of a patient on the burn unit. This 19-year-old young man had burns over 90 percent of his body. He died alone. His family was not allowed to visit because of the danger of infection. That was very hard. I will never forget that."

Suzanne Mary Alexander Owen
St. Vincent Hospital School of Nursing, Class of 1974

"…some very sad, like the 30-year-old mother of four that I took care of the last week of her life. I remember she was the only patient I ever saw who was conscious almost to the hour of her death. She gave instructions to her husband like she was leaving for a long trip. It was emotional but also a privilege to help her and the family."

Karen Steinmetz Christian
Maumee Valley Hospital School of Nursing, Class of 1968

"I remember a patient I had who was getting indwelling radiation therapy after surgical pelvic exoneration. This was very difficult for the patient and complicated her care. I went in to do her vital signs and she had some dried feces on her buttocks. My instructor helped me clean her up and she said to me, 'If you think this is ok nursing care, then just go home now.' I never forgot that. I learned a lot about skin integrity and patient dignity that day."

Diane Knoblauch
Toledo Hospital School of Nursing, Class of 1976

"I really liked clinicals. You always had your med cards with you because you were sure to be drilled on meds. Giving injections was easy for me because my mother was a diabetic and I had drawn up her insulin and given her shots … I was with a favorite patient when she died and I remember thinking, 'I hope I was a comfort to her.' I got permission to stay with her until she died."

Norma Provencher Lake
St. Vincent Hospital School of Nursing, Class of 1974

"At the time people thought flowers were not good in the rooms overnight, so they were placed in the hallways for the patient's good health. The night nurses changed the water and cut the dead blooms and then returned the flowers to the room before 7 a.m."

Mary Findlay Root
Robinwood Hospital School of Nursing, Class of 1943

174

"I remember our care plans had to have detail. Instructors wanted evidence that we knew what we were doing and could give good care ... I loved clinicals and being with patients and helping. It led me to a career in hospice nursing."

Linda Graver Lucas
Toledo Hospital School of Nursing, Class of 1984

"My best instructor was the one no one liked, but I could tell the doctors and other nurses respected her. I was caring for a patient who was supposed to get an antibiotic. Well, it wasn't up on the floor yet from pharmacy and I reported that to the nurse. When I told my instructor as I was reporting off, she said, 'It is not the RN's responsibility. It is yours.' That has always stayed with me. Even though our clinical time was done, she made me get the antibiotic from pharmacy and give it to the patient. She made our whole clinical group stay. But, it was my responsibility. I know I disappointed her but she was helping me learn responsibility for the patients I cared for"

Annette Mazzurco Hallett
Mercy Hospital School of Nursing, Class of 1984

"My classroom instructors were my clinical instructors. They knew how to correlate content to clinicals. I had at least 16 hours of clinicals per week. The instructors were very strict about skills, preparation and appearance. You had to know the medications, disease and nursing care because your instructor would quiz you. Yes, I was scared of some of them."

Anita Kowaski Cygnor
Mercy Hospital School of Nursing, Class of 1991

"I got into school right after high school. I was so naïve. My first clinical assignment was to give complete baths to two people. I cleaned off this dirt on both of their foreheads and thought I did a good job. Only later did I learn that it was Ash Wednesday and these ashes were a sacred

religious tradition. I just didn't know … We had to go to the floor the day before our clinicals. We would get our assignment and then prepare. We had to review the chart and list of all medications. Then we had to write out our plan of care and oh yes, the med cards."

Amy Smith
St. Vincent Hospital School of Nursing, Class of 1994

"Everybody stressed out the night before clinicals preparing care plans and med cards. Lots of Pepcid … Always emphasized patient first and patient privacy … Unprofessional to talk about patients outside the clinical setting … I worked weekends in the hospital to increase my skill competency."

Lissa Wilhelm Brehm
St. Vincent Hospital School of Nursing, Class of 1995

STUDENTS ON STRIKE

Given the significant control exerted by hospital administration and school of nursing hierarchies, the idea that students would strike because of unfairness was amazing. In 1916, student nurses at the Toledo Training School, later known as the Toledo Hospital School of Nursing, went on strike. Records are unclear about the exact nature of the dispute. One of the grievances was the wrongful dismissal of a student. Margaret Wallace, superintendent, defended the student's dismissal because the student was partially deaf and could not carry out her duties completely. Miss Wallace was remembered by students at the time as a woman who was unsympathetic, harsh, cruel, arrogant, and disrespectful of students, nurses, and physicians. It appears that her dismissal was the goal of this strike. The board of trustees held a much more favorable opinion of her and continued to support her throughout the strike.

The school's records show that on January 11, 1916, student nurses went on strike to dramatize the problems with Miss Wallace. It seems the students had the full support of physicians, who also were anxious to be rid of this superintendent. It is almost unimaginable how bad conditions for the students must have been to take such a drastic measure. Apparently all the students lined up at 7 p.m. by the floor to which they were assigned and filed out of the hospital floor by floor. They were accompanied by the medical staff who pledged not to send patients to the hospital until the differences were resolved. Thirty-seven student nurses went out on strike leaving seven nurses to care for 90 hospitalized patients. Help from other hospitals was offered and refused.

The students' attempts to have their grievances heard by the board were referred to Miss Wallace. A story in the Toledo Blade reported that she met with the students and criticized them severely, calling them "hussies, vixens, and ungrateful wretches."

The board members again refused to act on the nurses' demands because they had not followed the proper channels. The situation was so dire that meetings were held between city officials, physicians, and striking student nurses, and they discussed starting a municipal city-owned hospital staffed by the striking student nurses and angered physicians. A week into the strike saw no resolution, with Miss Wallace maintaining her position and some of the students returning to work for fear of being dismissed from the school.

The strike was still not resolved, and on March 6 a man

and his pregnant wife who was in labor approached the hospital but were turned away by Miss Wallace. The woman delivered a baby boy in the snow-covered street off the hospital property. Reports vary on why this couple was turned away but soon afterwards Miss Wallace resigned. The resignation was accepted by the board.

Students began returning to the school and hospital by mid-April. They were all able to make up missed days and to graduate. This ended a painful, bitter episode for them and the community.[16]

UNIFORMS

Rules and regulations governed clinical experiences and students' lives. Rules about uniforms were particularly detailed, specific, and inviolable. Early in the century, the admission packet that each student received with instructions about what to bring and what to expect of nursing school came with sewing directions. From St. Vincent Hospital:

"Probationers must bring with them the following…Three uniforms consisting of plain skirt with six-inch hem on bottom and a two-inch tuck. Skirt must be six inches from the floor and opened at the front, must not be gored and must be full in the back, waist and skirt being joined together. For a small nurse, skirt must be 62 inches in width, for a large nurse, skirt must be wider. Material must be well shrunken before being made up. Skirt of dress should have large pocket. It is not necessary to bring a sweater; the nurses wear the uniform nurses' cape. Aprons, bibs, collars and cuffs are ready made and can be secured from the Nurses Home. As shoes are an important

[16]Weiser, PJ, *A Legacy of Caring: A History of the Toledo Hospital School of Nursing*. (Toledo, OH: Wayne Graphics, 1988), 23-30.

In a picture from the St. Vincent School of Nursing yearbook, The Vincente 1898-1923, Alice Butler, Catherine Butler, and Jennie Butler, Class 1898, model the first uniform adopted by the school for student nurses. It was voluminous and handmade, most likely by the students themselves. (Photo courtesy of Mercy Health/St. Vincent archives)

part of the nurse's uniform, all probationers are requested to refrain from buying shoes for duty until entering the hospital. The hospital has arranged that the orthopedic surgeon will examine the feet of all probationers and prescribe the proper shoes. Examination will be free of charge."[17]

A later circular from this same school specifies that McCall's pattern 3205 for three dress uniforms. Joanna Russ recalled that Flower Hospital School of Nursing student uniforms followed a pattern by Butterick.

---

[17] The St. Vincent's Hospital Training School for Nurses Circular of Information (1921).

Students were to bring "two pairs comfortable white canvas oxfords with rubber heel." "Shoes should be purchased a few weeks before entering the training school and broken in. Shoes must be large. They will shrink when cleaned." Style changes were made throughout the years, and in 1963 St. Vincent replaced the starched student uniform with a cotton-polyester one.[18] By the time the last class graduated from a diploma school of nursing in Toledo, the student uniforms were one piece and made of no-iron materials. Male students wore similarly colored jackets and white pants.

"We wore our capes outside at Detroit Children's Hospital and on Cherry Street because those hospitals were in bad neighborhoods. The prostitutes would leave us alone and no one hurt us because they knew we were nurses and nurses helped them."

Mary Findlay Root
Robinwood Hospital School of Nursing, Class of 1943

"First memories of clinical were going to roll call in the chapel. Then taking vital signs on all patients in the old B wing and St. Vincent Hall (it had huge rooms with four to six patients to a room) and wearing stiffly starched uniforms."

Betty Spencer Lemon
St. Vincent Hospital School of Nursing, Class of 1958

---

[18]Compiled by The St. Vincent Medical Center School of Nursing and Alumni Association Centennial History Committee, A History of St. Vincent Medical Center School of Nursing 1896-1996, 14.

Student uniforms were made to be functional, usually with a pocketed apron or pinafore. Rules and regulations also assured that they were made to specification and looked alike. In fact, the skirt lengths are identical in this picture. (Photo courtesy of Mercy College of Ohio archives)

Later, uniforms were store bought with pants as an option. They were made from polyester and still very much alike. (Photo courtesy of ProMedica Toledo Hospital archives)

"Many of our instructors I found intimidating and threatening. They had a lot of power over if we passed or failed; even failing for something like a uniform being too short. Ours had to be at the middle of the knee and our hair up off our collar."

Janice Smith Cook
Flower Hospital School of Nursing, Class of 1976

"Our uniform aprons would get loaded down with care plans, med cards, pen light, bandage scissors, alcohol wipes, calipers, hemostats and other things."

Amy Smith
St. Vincent Hospital School of Nursing, Class of 1994

AFFILIATIONS

Affiliations were those clinicals student nurses obtained outside of their hospital. Schools of nursing entered into agreements with specialty hospitals and community health services to increase the breadth of student clinical experiences.

In the early years of diploma nursing education, a school might be part of a specialty hospital that only prepared a nurse for that specialty. Riverside Hospital School of Nursing, originally a women's and children's specialty hospital, had a diploma nursing school. In 1895, the course of study could be completed in four months. The program expanded to one year in 1896, and prepared the graduate to take care of women in all phases of pregnancy. In 1921, the hospital expanded the curriculum to three years to encompass a complete diploma nursing school education. Because the hospital was primarily a hospital for women giving birth and ill children, until 1945 all clinicals with adult patients had to be completed at other hospitals.[19]

Community nursing was an affiliation outside of the hospital. This experience was often coordinated with a visiting nurse association.

Many hospitals, not only in Toledo but across the country, did not have adequate clinical experiences for pediatric nursing or psychiatric nursing. These affiliations were obtained by going to a specialty hospital. Sometimes these hospitals were in the same city and other times students had to travel and stay in other cities for the duration of the experience.

In 1937, St. Vincent Hospital School of Nursing had a three month affiliation service for communicable diseases with Herman Kiefer Hospital in Detroit.[20] In Toledo, the psychiatric nursing experience was frequently obtained at the Toledo State Hospital on Arlington Avenue. Pediatrics was often an affiliation at a large children's hospital in Cincinnati, Columbus, Detroit, or Cleveland.[21]

"For my visiting nurse experience I was assigned to a downtown clinic. One day a week every prostitute had to have a vaginal exam. If

[19]Alumnae Association of Riverside Hospital School of Nursing, *Riverside Hospital Memories and Progress*, (1966).

[20]Compiled by The St. Vincent Medical Center School of Nursing and Alumni Association Centennial History Committee, *A History of St. Vincent Medical Center School of Nursing 1896-1996*, 9.

[21]Robinwood Hospital School of Nursing School Bulletin, (1906-1949), 5.

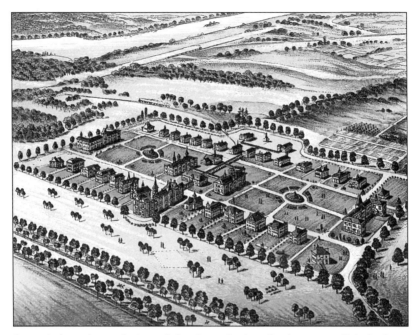

An artist's early rendering of the State Asylum for Insane or Toledo State Hospital which was on Arlington Avenue. Many of the Toledo Schools of Nursing did their psychiatric affiliations there. (Photo courtesy Mercy Health St. Vincent Archives)

they didn't show up, we reported them to the police and they went to pick them up. We were looking for venereal disease. We treated them with potassium permanganate douche. There were no antibiotics."

Alene Duerk
Toledo Hospital School of Nursing, Class of 1941

"We had a three month rotation at the Toledo State Hospital and had to live there. They had the best squash for dinner. The hospital was very, very noisy with patients screaming. I thought I would go crazy. Then one day I was taking a dinner tray into a patient who was in solitary confinement. I had an attendant with me because that was the

*procedure. You did not go alone. We found the patient had hung himself.
He was already dead when we found him."*

Alice U. Calabrese
St. Vincent School of Nursing, Class of 1950

*"We had pediatrics at Cincinnati Children's. It was my last rotation
and it broke my heart. We (student nurses) managed whole wards
with sick babies and parents weren't allowed to spend the night together.
We really didn't know what we were doing."*

Cassandra Willey Zak
Toledo Hospital School of Nursing, Class of 1972

*"I liked the psychiatric affiliation at Toledo State Hospital. We
moved to the nursing dorm on the campus of State Hospital. We were
mixed with many schools of nursing from everywhere."*

Barbara Halpin Adamczak
St. Vincent Hospital School of Nursing, Class of 1958

*"My psych experience was at Toledo State Hospital on Arlington.
Again, I was so young. Some of the experiences were both funny and
frightening at the same time. Like the patient who kept patting my head,
saying, 'Nice kitty.'"*

Amy Smith
St. Vincent Hospital School of Nursing, Class of 1994

Clinicals were experiences that were a strong part of diploma
nursing education. This strength gave graduates the confidence to work
in an often stressful environment caring for ill patients. Much of what
student nurses had learned and practiced in their basic education, they
would use again in their professional practice. They were well prepared
to practice as professional nurses in a hospital. As professional nursing
changed, so did clinicals. Throughout the century clinicals moved from
a mechanism to staff hospitals to model for applying classroom theory

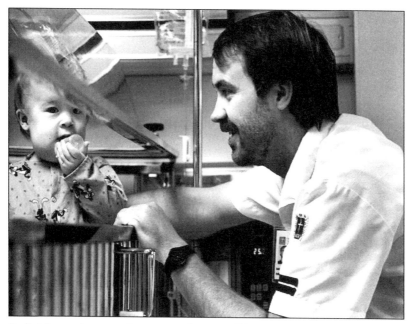

Pediatric nursing experience was often an affiliation or one that was done at another facility because the school's hospital did not care for that particular patient group. The children were usually eagerly anticipated as patients but not always easy to care for. Here a student from Mercy Hospital School of Nursing bonds with a pediatric patient. (Photo courtesy of the Mercy College of Ohio Archives)

to real-world patient care. Clinicals paralleled the evolution of hospitals and professional nursing.

"Hospitals wanted to hire diploma grads because we knew how to run a floor; we knew how to take care of patients. They taught us discipline and how to think like a nurse."

Suzanne Mary Alexander Owen
St. Vincent Hospital School of Nursing, Class of 1974

Chapter 6
Becoming...A Registered Nurse

"So, never lose an opportunity of urging a practical beginning, however small, for it is wonderful how often in such matters the mustard-seed germinates and roots itself."

– Florence Nightingale

GRADUATION

Graduation. The formal recognition of finishing nursing school. The culmination of years of study and clinicals. The official end to countless med cards, skill check lists, and being always ready to answer the question "What is your nursing priority today?" Graduation. The school's declaration that students have demonstrated the ability to think conceptually, plan holistically, and safely implement professional nursing care. Receiving the school pin and the black stripe for the school cap. A final opportunity for the class to publicly declare, through recitation of the Nightingale Pledge, their commitment to the values of professional nursing. A warm welcome into the alumni association. Graduation. A true commencement. An occasion that is worthy of the happiest celebration and a reminder that this day is only the beginning.

"Graduation was at the Paramount Theater downtown. It was very simple and very quick. It was the war years and we had to get back to work. Some couldn't attend the graduation ceremony because they were on duty."

Virginia Williams Whitmore
Lucas County Hospital School of Nursing, Class of 1943

During a 1982 graduation celebration at Toledo Hospital School of Nursing, students from other classes are also dressed in their uniforms. Kneeling, from left, Katherine Rogers and Linda Graver; standing, from left, Toledo Hospital Auxiliary President Suzanne Speck, Lori Ann Shook, Mary Schumann, Julie Sohnley, and the Director of Toledo Hospital School of Nursing, Margie Place. (Photo courtesy of Linda Graver Lucas).

"Graduation was a great day. We were finally nurses in white uniforms and caps with a black stripe."

Nancy R. Swartz
Riverside Hospital School of Nursing, Class of 1959

Nursing school graduation is often remembered in the abstract. Nurses most often remember receiving their school pin and that the occasion was full of relieved and joyous feelings shared with family and other loved ones. Graduation memories were usually not specific. What seems to be most often remembered in detail is the registered nurse licensing exam, known variously as State Board Exams or NCLEX-RN (National Council Licensure Examination for Registered Nurses.)

Passing this test is the final and essential step as it legally affirms a graduate's knowledge base as comprehensive enough to be called a Registered Nurse, and signing his or her name as R.N. It has not always been such a formal process. Nurse registration and mandatory testing in Ohio celebrated its one hundredth anniversary in 2016, 113 years after nursing schools began in Toledo.

"Graduation was good. But, we all knew the most important was next… The Test!"

Jeff Lycan
Toledo Hospital School of Nursing, Class of 1984

Graduation Day was a time of great joy and relief. Amy Jo Zimmerman smiles as she shows off her new diploma and pin. Circa 1980's. (Photo courtesy of Mercy Health/St. Vincent archives)

NURSE REGISTRATION IN OHIO

By the end of the nineteenth century, the advancement of scientific knowledge in the understanding of disease etiology and treatment was rapidly expanding. Systematic study of health and illness led to an explosion of medical and nursing knowledge in the twentieth century. To remain pertinent, nursing education needed to move beyond concepts of vocational training such as "occupation," "apprenticeship," and "trade." The ideal of a "calling" as solely sufficient to be called a nurse was widely questioned by nurse leaders who believed nursing should be recognized as a learned profession.[1] In the 1890s, calls for a registry of those who had completed a standard nursing curriculum and passed an approved examination were heard in Europe, South Africa, and the United States. The fundamental reason for nurse registration is public health safety.[2] The public should be able to expect that persons calling themselves "registered nurses" have demonstrated a basic level of knowledge and skill.

In Ohio, legislators did not accept these ideas with any enthusiasm. Beginning in 1905, bills to secure nurse registration repeatedly failed in the state legislature.[3] Those most vocally opposed to the idea of nursing as a legislatively defined profession were the Ohio Medical Association and state legislators. Physicians often owned small "hospitals" located in homes and offered "nurses training" to staff them. Generally, there was nothing approaching a curriculum in these training schools. The idea of a mandated course of study was rejected. The idea that nursing could be a separate profession from medicine, with an autonomous knowledge base, was unthinkable. Legislators, all male and all raised in a Victorian-

[1] Ellen Davidson Baer, "Key Ideas in Nursing's First Century," *American Journal of Nursing (AJN)* 112, no. 5 (2012).

[2] Ibid.

[3] Ohio Nurses Association, "A Glance at Ona's 100+ Year History," in *Ohio Nurses Association* (Columbus, Ohio: Ohio Nurses Association, 2013).

era culture, were confused, even repulsed, by the idea that women would want—and ought to be offered—the opportunity to earn a living and be recognized independently of a man.

In 1910, Dr. D.E. Haag reflected this thinking when he addressed the graduating class of Robinwood Hospital School of Nursing: "The greatest woman is she who brings a man a home. She is greater than the suffragette or the platform reformer. She is not permitted to sully her fair name or pollute her hands with the political ballot, but into all other fields of activity she may enter, and the doors of literature, science and the arts are not closed to her." [4]

Ohio passed their first Nurse Practice Act on April 27, 1915. It established what today is called the Ohio Board of Nursing and legislated three important concepts: a definition of nursing, nursing education requirements, and licensing standards. On January 11, 1916, the first nurses were registered in Ohio, and on December 13 and 14, 1916, the first nursing licensing exam was administered in the state. Those nurses graduating after January 1, 1917, were required to pass the examination to be registered. Those who graduated before 1917 were "grandfathered" into the registry. [5]

Defining the nursing profession was the foundation of the first and all subsequent nurse practice acts. That definition, stated by the American Nurses Association (ANA), was that "Nursing is the protection, promotion, and optimization of health and abilities, prevention of illness and injury, facilitation of healing, alleviation of suffering through the diagnosis and treatment of human response, and advocacy in the care of individuals, families, groups, communities, and populations." [6]

A little-known fact is that mandatory licensure of registered nurses

---

[4]Toledo Times, "Robinwood Nurses' Graduating Service: Address By. Dr. D.E. Haag on the Duties of the Nurse," news release, July 1, 1910, 1910.

[5]Association.

[6]American Nurses Association, "What Is Nursing? ," American Nurses Association, http://www. nursingworld.org/EspeciallyForYou/What-is-Nursing.

did not begin in Ohio until January 1, 1968. It took 51 years for Ohio to fully protect the public health by requiring demonstration of a minimal competency through nurse registration and licensure by the state. Only those who passed this exam could legally call themselves "registered nurses." The term "trained nurse" was used to describe a graduate nurse who did not take, or successfully pass, the licensing exam.[7] Sustaining competency following licensure through mandatory continuing education was not required in Ohio until 1988.[8]

THE REGISTERED NURSE LICENSING EXAMINATION

Nurse registration laws were only the first step. Once passed, the laws were a signal to schools of nursing that educational preparation required consistency from program to program. Standardization of nursing school curricula was necessary to prepare graduates for the licensing exam.[9]

For the 1916 nursing registration exam, three nurses from the original members of the Ohio "Nurses' Examining Committee" wrote the questions. Candidates followed the Rules Governing Examination. A 75 percent average was required to pass the nine-section essay exam, and no grade at all was given for a score lower than 60 percent. [10] Three nurses achieved a passing score on that first exam.

Rules Governing Examination: December 13-14, 1916

1.   Applicant shall be known by number only

[7]James H. Rodabaugh and Mary Jane Rodabaugh, *Nursing in Ohio: A History* (Columbus, Ohio: The Ohio State Nurses Association, 1951).

[8]State of Ohio Legislature, "Ohio Administrative Code Chapter 4723," in *Chapter 4723*, ed. Ohio Board of Nursing (Columbus, Ohio 2016).

[9]Jane E. Murdock, "Evolution of the Nursing Curriculum," *Journal of Nursing History* 2, no. 1 (1986).

[10]Ohio Board of Nursing, "1916-the First Examination for Nurse Licensure," *Momentum* 13, no. 3 (2015).

2. Assigned numbers are to be used on all papers
3. Candidates are requested not to bring books or papers into the examination room
4. Paper and other examination materials will be provided by the Committee
5. Question papers must be returned with the answers
6. Write on one side of the paper only
7. Leave a line between each answer
8. Do not copy questions
9. Put a number of question in margin and number your answers in accordance
10. Examination papers will not be returned to applicant
11. Giving or receiving assistance or communication between candidates will be cause for dismissal
12. Candidates will be required to pass a general average of 75 percent with no grade below 60 percent

Sections and Examples of questions on the first Ohio nurse licensure examination

1. Anatomy and Physiology
   a. Describe the lungs. Name and locate the organs of the abdominal cavity.
2. Hygiene, Sanitation and Bacteriology
   a. Name and describe the different methods of sterilization. Which is the most effective in the shortest time?
3. Materia Medica and Therapeutics
   a. How would you prepare a 1% cocaine solution from a 4% solution?
4. Cookery and Dietetics
   a. How would you modify milk? State the correct methods of preparing tea, coffee, albumen water and cocoa

5. Nursing of Medical and Communicable Diseases
   a. Describe the general nursing care for a patient with diphtheria
6. Surgical Nursing
   a. Describe the preparation of a room for an immediate surgical emergency. What difference would you make in the preparation of the same room for an operation the next day?
7. Pediatric Nursing
   a. Describe the care of nursing bottles and rubber nipples. Why should a baby never be left alone to nurse from a bottle?
8. Obstetrical Nursing
   a. What would you do for a pregnant woman in convulsions until the physician arrives?
9. Ethics of Nursing
   a. If your patient didn't like you, what would you do?

In 1921, the exam was changed to three days. In 1941, the essay exam was changed to a 100-point multiple choice examination in nine subjects taken over two days. The United States' involvement in World War II increased the demand for nurses in the armed forces. Objective test questions were easier to grade and could speed up nurses' full enlistment in the military.[11] The new test format was known as the State Board Nursing Exam, or "State Boards." In 1946, Ohio began using the National League State Board Test Pool to choose exam questions. In 1950, nursing became the first profession to use the same licensure examination across the country. Although the State Board Test Pool questions were uniform, passing scores differed by state.[12] Licensure

---

[11] Elizabeth L. Kemble; Emma Spaney, "State Board Test Pool Examination," *American Journal of Nursing (AJN)* 47, no. 8 (1947).

[12] Elizabeth L. Kemble and Emma Spaney, "State Board Test Pool Examinations," ibid. pg. 552-554

was granted state by state, with some exceptions for reciprocity. The test was offered twice per year, on the same days, throughout the country. In Ohio, State Boards were taken in Columbus.

To say that State Boards were important is to understate the experience. The stress is remembered decades later. All nurses who showed evidence that they had graduated from an accredited school of nursing assembled together for the two-day examination. Proctors carefully observed thousands of graduates as they completed test booklets in six, and later, five subject areas. The subject areas closely mirrored the medical model of disease and health. The State Board Test Pool Examination categories were: Medical Nursing, Surgical Nursing, Pediatric Nursing, Obstetric Nursing, Psychiatric Nursing, and Communicable Disease (this content was integrated in 1955).

In 1978, the National Council of State Boards of Nursing assumed responsibility for the State Boards. [13]

In 1982, the State Board Exam test name was changed to National Council Licensure Examination or NCLEX. Test questions were organized in four nursing centered, instead of five medically focused categories. Those categories are: Safe and Effective Care Environment, Health Promotion and Maintenance, Psychosocial Integrity and Physiological Integrity [14]

Although it is difficult to explain the differences in focus between the State Board Test Pool questions and the NCLEX questions, a registered nurse will no doubt be able to identify the shift of question topics from medical model decision making to those which are nursing focused. [15, 16]

---

[13]Diane Benefiel, "The Story of Nurse Licensure," *Nurse Educator* 36, no. 1 (2011). Pg. 17

[14]Kaplan Testing Service, "Kaplan Test Preparation for the NCLEX" (2016).

[15]ANCC Nurse Credentialing, "Medical Surgical Sample Test," *ANCC Nurse Credentialing* (2016).

[16]NCLEX Exam Secrets Test Prep Team, *The NCLEX Flash Card Study System: NCLEX Practice Questions and Exam Review* (Momedia Metrix, 2013).

Sample State Board Questions:

1. The most common, preventable complication of abdominal surgery is:
   A. Atelectasis
   B. Fluid and electrolyte imbalance
   C. Thrombophlebitis
   D. Urinary retention

2. The main goal of treatment for acute glomerulonephritis is to:
   A. Encourage activity
   B. Encourage high protein intake
   C. Maintain fluid balance
   D. Teach intermittent urinary catheterization

3. Andrea with suspected rheumatic fever is admitted to the pediatric unit. When obtaining the child's history, the nurse considers which information to be most important?
   A. Fever that started 3 days ago
   B. Lack of interest in food
   C. A recent diagnosis of Strep throat
   D. Vomiting for 2 days

Sample NCLEX Questions:

1. What is the upper limit for a normal triglyceride level?
   A. 160
   B. 190
   C. 200
   D. 230

2. Delirium in the older adult can be a serious problem because it can:
    A. signal an underlying mental health disorder
    B. be linked to a disturbance in sleep
    C. impair motor activity
    D. be a symptom of a serious physical problem

3. When developing a plan of care for a male adolescent, the nurse considers the child's psychosocial needs. During adolescence, psychosocial development focuses on:
    A. Becoming industrious
    B. Establishing an identity
    C. Achieving intimacy
    D. Developing initiative

In 1982, the number of NCLEX test questions decreased from 720 to 480, and the number of questions decreased again to 370 in 1983. NCLEX remained a 2-day paper and pencil examination until 1994.

"Because World War II made travel difficult, I made arrangements to take my State Boards in Missouri. I had moved to St. Louis to continue my education and took Boards there in the fall. I passed on the first attempt."

Mary Ann Shea Arquette
St. Vincent Hospital School of Nursing, Class of 1942

"We could sign our name as Graduate Nurse or G.N. until we passed boards and became an R.N. I had to get special permission to take boards after graduation, because I wasn't 21 years old until December and boards were earlier in the year."

Nancy R. Swartz
Riverside Hospital School of Nursing, Class of 1959

"I went to Columbus to take my State Boards. They were in a big barn at the Ohio State Fairgrounds. My daughter was born a few days after I finished Boards. I was a little late for the second day of testing and many were worried that I delivered. So, when I walked into the testing room, many clapped."

Linda Shaw
St. Vincent Hospital School of Nursing, Class of 1974

Computers changed the way nurses were tested for competency. Because computers could be programmed to analyze test answers as they are chosen, it became possible to increase or decrease test question difficulty based on the answer to a previous question. This is called "adaptive testing." NCLEX as a Computer Adaptive Test (CAT) and was first offered on April 1, 1994, and it allowed NCLEX to be customized to the knowledge level of the graduate nurse. It allowed NCLEX to be given in six hours or less rather than two days.

NCLEX can also be taken by appointment at a testing center rather than twice per year in a central location. The graduate nurse can answer as few as 75 questions to demonstrate competency, or up to 265 questions. NCLEX CAT knows when competency is achieved and the computer turns off the exam. Rather than the same test given to thousands of nurses on the same day, each test is different. Numeric scores are now obsolete. The graduate nurse achieves Pass or Fail, and receives results in a few days, not months.[17] In 1994, nursing was the only profession to use CAT for entry level testing.[18]

"NCLEX changed to a computer test the year before I graduated. I remember being scared when the computer shut off after 75 questions. I

---

[17]Editor Jill Johnson, "Pencils Down, Booklets Closed," *In Focus* 1, no. 2 (2014).
[18]Ibid.

later learned that this was a good indicator that I had probably passed. I did pass!"

Lissa Wilhelm Brehm
St. Vincent Hospital School of Nursing, Class of 1995

NURSING EDUCATION EVOLUTION

Closing the Diploma Schools in Toledo

In Ohio, the early twentieth century was devoted to creating a formal recognition structure for the registered nurse. The Nurse Practice Act encompassed not only the definition of a professional registered nurse, but also the knowledge and skills nursing students were expected to learn. These formed the learning standards that had to be met to move to the next level in recognition: the licensing exam, and ultimately, registration.

Until the mid-twentieth century, diploma nursing programs were the mainstay of nursing education. This changed in 1948 with the publication of the Brown report. [19] This report recommended that professional nurses be educated in a collegiate setting. While the report was insightful, nurse educators and hospitals widely ignored it.[20] The momentum shifted in 1965 when the American Nurses Association published *A Position Paper on Educational Preparation for Nurse Practitioners and Assistants to Nurses.*[21] Commonly called the ANA's First Position Paper on Education for Nurses, it envisioned the baccalaureate degree in nursing (BSN) for entry level in professional (registered) nursing and an associate degree in nursing (ADN) for entry into the technical nursing level. Diploma nursing programs were not mentioned.

---

[19]Sister Rosemary Donely and Sister Mary Jean Flaherty, "Revisiting the American Nurses Association's First Paper on Education for Nurses," *Online Journal of Issues in Nursing* 7, no. 2 (2002).

[20]Ester Lucile Brown, "The Brown Report," *American Journal of Nursing (AJN)* 48, no. 12 (1948).

[21]Rita Munley Gallagher and Kaye Sullivan, "Compendium of ANA Education Positions, Position Statements and Documents ", ed. American Nurses Association (New York: American Nurses Publishing, 1996).

The reaction to this report was shock and outrage from diploma nursing educators and graduates. Default demotion of the diploma nurse to the role of "technical nurse" was especially insulting. In 1964, 72 percent of all nursing students were enrolled in hospital based diploma schools.[22]

The ANA continued to solidify the stand for baccalaureate nursing education as the entry level for professional nursing. ANA position statements and arguments supporting them continued unabated. In 1984, a specific timeline was put in place. By 1995, one hundred percent of all states were to have committed to requiring two levels of nursing practice and enforcing the concept of the BSN as the only entry level for professional registered nursing.

This goal was not met. However, the Toledo diploma schools of nursing recognized the financial constraints of declining student enrollment and the pressures exerted by the professional organization. Schools began closing. In 1999, St. Vincent Hospital School of Nursing was the last hospital based diploma school of nursing to close in Toledo.

The full recommendations of the ANA position papers have not been adopted. There are not two levels of nurses in the United States. Not all diploma schools have closed in Ohio. In 2016, the Ohio State Board of Nursing reported 11 approved diploma nursing programs in the state. Two of these programs are in northwest Ohio; one is in Toledo. Both diploma nursing schools are designed for the Licensed Practical Nurse (LPN) to achieve the additional knowledge and skills required to take the NCLEX and become a Registered Nurse. [23] Neither is hospital based. In Toledo, there are three BSN granting programs and two ADN programs.[24]

---

[22]Flaherty. Pg 4

[23]Ohio Board of Nursing, "Registered Nurse (RN) Program List," (Columbus, Ohio 2016).

[24]Ibid.

"Much to my amazement, I began supervising student nurses in my first job. That was commonly done because there were few nursing faculty then. I enjoyed teaching and was very interested in the NLN (National League for Nursing) standards for nursing school accreditation. I needed more education and so went back to school for a BSN and then a MSN."

E. Wanda Foltz Quay
Robinwood Hospital School of Nursing, Class of 1948

"Although very few Mary Manse College courses transferred, I knew I wanted to go on. Twenty years after graduation, I received a BSN."

Sharon Kitchen Viers
Mercy Hospital School of Nursing, Class of 1966

"I remember how hard nursing school was...it was all consuming. Yet, I knew I had to continue my education and so I went back to school and earned a BSN and then a master's degree."

Jeanne Ann Calabrese Drouillard
Mercy Hospital School of Nursing, Class of 1983

"I wouldn't have chosen any other program. I came out prepared to care for patients. But, I knew my education didn't end with my diploma. I went back to school soon after and eventually earned a master's degree in Nursing."

Anita Kowaski Cygnor
Mercy Hospital School of Nursing, Class of 1994

IMPACT OF TOLEDO DIPLOMA NURSE GRADUATES

Virtually everyone knows a diploma educated nurse who has had a positive influence on the community. Perhaps that nurse was a family member who always knew what to look for and what to do when someone became ill or injured, or was the nurse assigned when a baby was born or who provided a compassionate presence when a loved one died. She or he was a nurse who knew how to listen without judgment when listening was exactly what was needed, or the nurse who showed how to change a dressing or give the insulin or figure out how to follow a difficult new diet. He or she was thought of as the best nurse to ask when you needed to know the name of a "good" doctor, or whether you could benefit from a second opinion. The diploma nurse may be remembered as the most organized person on a committee or the person you could count on to help with the annual March for Babies or Girl Scout cookie fundraiser.

There were over 13,000 nurses who graduated from Toledo's diploma nursing schools.[25] It is not possible to identify the best of those nurses. There are too many who have made, and continue to make, it easier for others to live life in the best possible health. Every day, Toledo diploma nurses quietly go about working with patients and contributing to mental and physical health wherever they find themselves. They do not boast about their accomplishments. They do as Florence Nightingale inspired them to do: "I think one's feelings waste themselves in (mere) words. They ought to be distilled into actions which bring results." [26]

Toledo diploma nurses have made an impact within Toledo, the state of Ohio, the United States, and the world. There are many such nurses. It is not possible to individually recognize every one. Here are just a few examples.

---

[25] Joanna Russ, "Diploma Education for Nurses," in *Medicine on the Maumee: A History of Health Care in Northwest Ohio*, ed. Editor Barbara Floyd (Toledo, Ohio: The University of Toledo/ Ward M. Canaday Center for Special Collections, 2012).

[26] Alex Attewell, *Illuminating Florence: Finding Nightingale's Legacy in Your Practice* (Indianapolis, Indiana: Sigma Theta Tau International 2012). Pg. 8

Admiral Alene Duerk: A Graduate with International Influence

A 1941 graduate of the Toledo Hospital School of Nursing, Alene B. Duerk was just 25 years old in August 1945. Yet she was already a Registered Nurse, serving as a Lieutenant in the United States Navy. On that afternoon, she stood on the deck of the *U. S. S. Benevolence*, a Navy hospital ship, anchored in Tokyo Bay. For hours, small boats called "Liberty Ships" began arriving, one-after-another, filled with hundreds of young men. These were "survivors:"

Duerk

American soldiers who had been held captive during World War II in Omori and Shinagawa, two of Japan's most brutal prisoner of war camps.

In the 36 hours that followed, Alene and the small hospital ship staff triaged more than 1,200 American prisoners of war before providing their means of transportation back to America and "home" to their families. Alene recounts, "Those young men were in terrible shape when they came aboard. They were severely malnourished, infested with lice. Many suffered tuberculosis, Beri-Beri and deeply neglected wounds. We felt privileged to be there to care for them and to welcome them home." This unforgettable moment in America's history was just one of many unforgettable moments throughout Alene's highly decorated career in nursing.

Alene was born March 29, 1920, to Albert and Emma Duerk, of Defiance, Ohio. Alene, and her younger sister, Evelyn, grew up in the small town of Holgate, Ohio. Their father served America on the battlefields of France during World War I. There, he was exposed to mustard gas—a debilitating injury from which he never fully recovered. Returning home after the war, he required constant care until he passed in 1925.

Toledo Hospital School of Nursing Pin

Alene, her sister, and her mother provided him the care they could. However, it was the Visiting Nurses who regularly came to their home who provided invaluable comfort. Alene, just a small child at the time, was mesmerized by these nurses who were helpful, kind, and capable. Alene was intrigued by their uniforms, and by instruments they carried with them. Alene remembers, "At the time, I kept wondering—what all do they carry in that big, black bag? What else is in there? I was so curious!" The positive influence of these Visiting Nurses inspired Alene as she grew older. Already, she sensed being called to service, and before long, she would realize that "call" might be best satisfied through serving others as a nurse. In time, both Alene and her sister Evelyn chose to make nursing their career.

When Alene graduated from high school, she had the grades to go on to the University of Michigan. However, furthering her education there was financially, and geographically out of reach. A friend suggested

Robinwood Hospital School of Nursing Pin

Alene consider the Toledo Hospital School of Nursing. After investigation, Alene interviewed at the school. Her application was quickly accepted and her formal nursing education began.

Alene fondly remembers her time spent at Toledo Hospital School of Nursing. However, she said, "There was little time for fun."

Classroom and clinical experience was intense. "I made wonderful friends there, of course, and there were instructors I deeply admired. However, I took my studies seriously. It was important to learn as much as I could, while I could."

While in Toledo, the two clinical rotations Alene remembers most clearly were the psychiatric nursing experience at Toledo

Riverside Hospital School of Nursing Pin

State Hospital and the community nursing rotation with the Visiting Nurses. At the state hospital, Alene was assigned to "Night Duty" at the Women's Psychiatric Ward. In community nursing, she was assigned to a downtown free clinic. The venues offered vastly different nursing experience, yet were equally beneficial to her education.

In the spring of 1941, Alene graduated from Toledo Hospital School of Nursing and went on to pass the Ohio State Nursing Board Examination. Just a few months later, on December 7, 1941, Japan shocked the world when they bombed Pearl Harbor, and the United States entered World War II. At that time, sentiment was high in support

of the war effort. So Alene, like many of her classmates, enlisted in the military. Alene chose to join the Navy, and during World War II, was assigned to serve in naval hospitals within the continental United States.

When World War II ended, the Navy assigned Alene to the naval hospital in Great Lakes, Illinois. However, the Navy quickly realized

Mercy Hospital School of Nursing Pin

they needed fewer nurses after the war, and Alene was discharged. Seizing the moment to advance her education, and thanks to the G. I. Bill, Alene chose to spend this time completing her Bachelor of Science at Case Western Reserve University's Francis Payne Bolton School of Nursing in Cleveland.

Upon completion of her studies, Alene relocated to Detroit, where she was employed as "Supervisor and Nursing Instructor" at Highland Park General Hospital. Though now formally a civilian, Alene had remained active in a local Navy Military Reserve Unit. When the Korean War broke out in 1950, the Navy re-called Alene back to active duty.

During the Korean War, Alene was stationed in Portsmouth, Virginia, where she trained medical corpsmen at the Hospital Corps School. It was in this assignment Alene found her passion. She thoroughly enjoyed teaching young medical corpsmen. In her next assignment, which would take her to Philadelphia, Alene developed an in-service education program for Navy hospital corpsmen who were eventually assigned to naval hospitals throughout the country and abroad.

When the Korean War ended in 1953, Alene remained on active military duty. Her assignments ranged from serving at the naval hospital in Bethesda, Maryland (where she saw the first artificial eye implanted) to serving as a "Navy Nurse Recruiter" in downtown Chicago.

Maumee Valley Hospital School of Nursing Pin

At the beginning of the Vietnam War, Alene continued her upward career path in promotion and responsibility as a "Charge Nurse" at Subic Bay Station Hospital in the Philippines.

No stranger to adventure, Alene also volunteered, along with a few Navy doctors and dentists, to periodically helicopter into the thick jungles of the Philippine mountains to render medical care and medicine to remote villagers, including to those who lived in leper colonies in remote regions of the Philippines. Such above-and-beyond service required tremendous physical stamina and the willingness to sacrifice any and all personal comforts. These committed few made a tremendous humanitarian difference to the

St. Vincent Hospital School of Nursing Pin

Philippine people, and enhanced diplomatic relations between the United States Navy and the Philippines' government.

In 1963, the Navy transferred Alene to Yokosuka, Japan, where she was promoted to "Assistant Chief Nurse and Commander." An even bigger opportunity came in 1968 when Alene was assigned to the Pentagon in Washington, D. C. as liaison between military nurses and the Assistant Director for Health and Environmental at the Pentagon. In 1970, Alene was promoted to the rank of captain.

On April 26, 1972, President Richard Nixon promoted Alene B. Duerk to the rank of rear admiral, making her the first woman in the history of the United States Navy to be promoted to admiral.

Alene retired from the U. S. Navy in 1975. She spent her final years at the Bureau of Medicine and Surgery in Washington, D. C., promoting and encouraging women to enter the field of nursing, especially by serving their country.

Though being promoted to the

Flower Hospital School of Nursing Pin

rank of rear admiral made Alene somewhat of an overnight celebrity throughout the United States, she never relaxed in that role. Instead, she wore her rank as a workhorse accepts a heavy yoke. From Alene's perspective, she had assumed the responsibility to represent military and civilian nurses with only the highest level of integrity. Alene said she rose every morning with a determination to perform all personal and professional duties in a way that would guarantee the legacy she left behind would illuminate a pathway that other women would be eager to tread.

Alene, now 97, enjoys her retirement in Lake Mary, Florida. She remains active in the community there, having worked tirelessly for many years with the Visiting Nurse Association Board and on behalf of the Central Florida College of Nursing. In addition, an endowed student nursing scholarship in her name has been established at the University of Central Florida. She remains an active member of her church and is revered and loved throughout her community.

Alene was recently asked if she was saddened upon hearing of the closure of the Toledo Hospital School of Nursing. She replied, "Of course, no one likes to see good things come to an end. However, we all serve for a season and when I needed a good school of nursing, Toledo Hospital provided me an excellent start. For a very long time, it provided many nurses with opportunity they might not have otherwise had. I'm happy the school was there while it was; it served a powerful purpose for a very long time."

As for advice for women in nursing today, Alene said, "I'm concerned when I hear young nurses saying they're "discouraged" with nursing. I think so many of them feel a career in nursing only locks you into day-to-day hospital work, and that's the end of it. However, opportunity in nursing is, and always has been, limited only by one's imagination. I encourage nurses today to seek opportunity, to try new things. It's important nurses remain challenged, and excited, about what they're doing. If you ever lose your enthusiasm, or get to the point you 'dread' going to work, then, it's time to find another occupation. Nursing is not about accolades or benefits; it's about having a heart for service. It's being willing to get your hands dirty even when you know, in advance, the task will be thankless. Nursing is about finding your own happiness in the pure privilege of helping others who need it. A great nurse will be content as 'servant to all'...regardless of rank."

Alice Miller: A Pioneer in Health Care Research

Miller

Alice Miller, by her own admission, is a risk taker. Her nursing career, both military and civilian, seemed to always be on the forefront. As a caregiver, professional nurse, and leader she has had plenty of practice taking risks.

Alice graduated from the Toledo Hospital School of Nursing in the summer of 1941. After the bombing of Pearl Harbor, Alice recalls, "Three quarters of my classmates joined the military. Me? I wanted to join but I was only 20 years old and you had to be 22. I wasn't even able to take State Boards until I was 21 years old. So, I worked on a surgical unit until I was old enough. Then I joined the Navy. They promised I 'would see the world' and I wanted that."

Her first stop was boot camp training at Bethesda Naval Hospital. "It taught me how to run a unit, march, and salute." She was further trained to work on a hospital ship. This included lifesaving activities. "Lifesaving meant for yourself and your patients," she said. These skills were tested by jumping off a high diving board, swimming, and getting onto a raft without upsetting it.

She remembers one of the accidents she was called to early in her military career while stationed in Jacksonville, Florida. A plane had crashed into the river; all aboard died still sitting in their seats. How do you respond to such a tragedy? "You do what you're supposed to do; what you were trained to do," she says simply.

In 1945 she was assigned to a hospital ship, the *USS Solace*. The *Solace* was anchored near battle grounds in the Pacific arena and the wounded were brought aboard in small boats. A hospital ship is considered by the terms of the Geneva Convention to be immune from attack in war. Yet, each night the hospital ship would move out to sea, away from the other ships, in case of enemy fire. One night, a Japanese raider pilot targeted their ship even though it was well illuminated.

Alice remembers, "You just knew it was coming in. The plane had a different sound. How he missed us I will never know." After that near-miss incident, the ship stayed anchored with the Third Fleet day and night for protection. "One night, the fleet was attacked, and we were there," she recalls. "It was a frightening experience."

She made seven trips from Okinawa to Guam transporting more than 400 patients each time. By historic accounts, the Battle of Okinawa was one of the fiercest and bloodiest of the World War II. It lasted 82 days with injuries often horrendous. After stabilization on the hospital ship, the most severely injured patients were transported to San Francisco for care.

Over seven decades later, one thing she is still disappointed about is that she was on leave in Ohio when the World War II peace treaty was signed. Their ship had been docked for repairs and the crew dispersed around the country on leave. They missed the historic moment. It felt like "we did all the work but missed the celebration." They were not there to help rescue the released POWs. Their efforts had done much to help during the fighting but, to Alice, this still felt unfinished.

Today she is an outspoken opponent of war. "War is never good. All these young men; they had dreams," she says emotionally. While caring for the seriously wounded, often in the burn unit, she would provide physical and emotional comfort to young men whose dreams were now changed and perhaps shattered. Seventy-five years later she still remembers one of them asking, "Miss Miller, do you think I can still be a Shakespearean actor?" He had a shrapnel wound which destroyed half of his buttocks.

After the war, she did not re-enlist. In 1947, she felt that four and a half years was enough. She felt "too regimented, too much being told what to do." Once discharged from the U.S. Navy, she enrolled at Case Western Reserve University's Frances Payne Bolton School of Nursing and completed her Bachelor of Science in Nursing degree. The GI Bill enabled her to go to college.

She taught for a year at Silver Cross Hospital School of Nursing in Joliet, Illinois, and then joined the staff of University of Chicago Hospital where she worked for 20 years. During her tenure at the University of Chicago, she was part of the team which opened the first research unit in the United States funded by the National Institutes of Health. On this unit, she recalls caring for a patient with leprosy and many others with diabetes and cancer.

At the University of Chicago hospitals, Alice had three different positions: nursing supervisor for patient care and x-ray technicians in the Radiology Department, Assistant Director of Nursing and, her favorite, Director of the Operating Room. She liked jobs that were fast-paced and active. She earned her master's degree in 1961 from the Washington School of Nursing, in Seattle. In 1970, she moved to Tucson, Arizona. As the Associate Director of Staff Development, she helped set up the new University Hospital at the University Medical Center. Alice retired in 1983.

Alice recalls the many changes in nursing that occurred during her career. While nursing around the United States, she observed new drugs and advances in nursing and medical care. Patients were ambulated and moving sooner following illness, surgery, and trauma. Complications decreased. Alice's advanced degrees in nursing were unusual for the time. Through higher education and expert clinical practice, she helped pave the way for nurses to participate in research. Alice's career started as a diploma school of nursing graduate but it did not stop there. Her contributions were appreciated by military and civilian patients alike.

Mary Ann Shea Arquette: A Graduate who Recorded her own Story of Nursing School

Arquette

A 1942 graduate of the St. Vincent Hospital School of Nursing, Mary Ann Shea Arquette agreed to an interview in 2015. Before the interview began, she was reading a 1,250-page book, *The History of the American Red Cross*, published in 1922. While enjoying it, she pointed out, "This book is just slightly younger than I am!" At the age of 94, she is still proud of her diploma nursing education. Although some depict hospitals that took advantage of student nurses through diploma education, Mary Ann is adamant, "I never felt like that. Yes. We worked hard but I got good education." She describes the tenor of the times: To do what was expected and to do it well. "The word 'training' to describe our educational program was acceptable then. Various words identified not only who we were, but what we did. Doctors 'doctored' and nurses 'nursed.' Teachers taught and student nurses learned, or they wouldn't be students very long. Every school adhered to standards. In those days, when the gatekeepers of the nursing school (the Director and Faculty), approved an applicant as eligible to join their ranks, apparently, they had done their duty and the rest was up to the student. The expectation was that the student nurse would meet the standards. Nothing less was expected and no accolades were given for doing what was expected."

Throughout her life, education was important. The same year she graduated, she and a classmate boarded a train for St. Louis University, which accepted 35 college credits from St. Vincent Hospital School of Nursing. This was far more than universities in the Toledo area. Mary Ann earned a Bachelor's of Science in Nursing Education (BSNE) and then, a Master of Arts with a major in Counseling and Guidance from the former Mary Manse College, in Toledo.

An unpublished autobiographical account, *My Life So Far* [27] speaks eloquently of her experiences. The following are excerpts:

- The day they started training, August 16, 1939, Mary Ann and a classmate went to see the movie *The Wizard of Oz* downtown at the Paramount Theater. "Of course we were back by the appointed hour and followed the rigidity of 9:45 p.m. in the building, 10:00 p.m. in your room, and 10:15 p.m. lights out. It didn't take long for all the nursing students to realize that only your illness on the premises, or maybe death (all of which had to be proved) could cause those times to be adjusted."

- "Incoming class members were called Probationers, usually abbreviated to 'Probies.' We remained Probies until the end of the first semester of classes. Those who survived to continue in the program were then called freshmen."

- "All students were required to buy bandage scissors and their own hypodermic syringes/needles, as well as their own wrist-watches, each with a second hand. Students bought their caps, cape, and uniforms through the School of Nursing. The assessment for these items was included in the bills from the school. Although we did not have to

---

[27] Mary Ann Arquette, "My Life So Far," (unpublished, c. manuscript 2007-2010), 18.

buy thermometers, we were required to pay for any that we broke."

- "On the fifth floor of the School of Nursing Building, one classroom was designated as the Nursing Arts lab. During our first year, we had many classes in that room. It was equipped with several beds which housed (mannequin patients) Mr. Chase and Mrs. Chase and a crib for Baby Chase. I presume they were purchased from a company called Chase."

- "In our first month as students, we were taught Printing and Charting. Since handwriting varies, printing was required. However, each of us developed our own style. The criterion was readability. We also learned that 'If it isn't written, it wasn't done.' Since a patient's chart (record), could be used in a court of law, this was 'pounded' into us."

- "This was the era of the Great Depression. Rubber gloves were washed with soap, and mended with glue and patches made from other gloves which otherwise could not be salvaged. The repaired gloves were matched for size and placed in cloth packages with size marked on the outside. Like the pledgets and the applicators, the gloves were then autoclaved in Central Service and furnished on call to the various departments."

- "I remember that my watch was a Timex. It cost $3.25. It ran perfectly until the day of graduation. Then it stopped and was declared unfixable. My dad bought me a new watch the next day."

- "When we were students we were to be called Miss along with our surnames. Married women were not admitted to this school at this time. While we were on duty, or in the classroom, we were never to use our first names when we addressed each other, or when anyone else addressed us.

Consequently, we called each other by our last names all the time, skipping the 'Miss' of course. Even now all these years later, when I think of my classmates and all the other nurses I knew at that time, I first think of them by their last names. Those habits are hard to change."

Although some of the etiquette for nurses and our world has changed, the patient focus remains. We are fortunate that Mary Ann's legacy is documented in her memoirs.

Mary Booker Gregory: A Graduate who Tore Down a Barrier

Being first is never easy. For a young woman who never sought the spotlight, Mary Booker Gregory Powell unwittingly and graciously has served as a role model for African Americans who want to become registered nurses. At the time, the attention paid to her as the first African American to attend and graduate from a Toledo nursing school was not easy.

Gregory

Born February 1, 1930, in Marion, Indiana, Mary moved to Toledo with her parents when she was 12 years old. Looking back, Mary said she was prepared for just about anything after graduating in 1947 from Libbey High School. She was not prepared, though, for being denied entrance to five schools of nursing in Toledo. Denied admission without explanation, she and four other African American women who were also rejected from Toledo diploma nursing schools attended University of Toledo for one year.

Her four friends went on to graduate from University of Toledo as pharmacists and teachers. Mary was the only one to reapply to nursing schools the following year. Again, she was denied admission. Her transcripts were returned unopened. Mid-twentieth century admission decisions allowed exclusion based on race. Although this blatant discrimination was documented as early as the 1920's[28] [29], it continued unabated in Toledo until Mary Booker received a phone call on a Friday in 1948 telling her she could start nursing school the following Monday. Mary is not certain why this one school reversed their decision, but a weekend before the first day of class Mary was accepted at St. Vincent Hospital School of Nursing.

As a student nurse, Mary quickly learned the importance of proving herself. She recalls she had to constantly outperform others' expectations of a student nurse. She chose to look at this as an opportunity to shine rather than worry about the possibility of failure. She remembers that the school of nursing administration and faculty were supportive and encouraging.

Physicians and other nurses in the hospital were not always as respectful. Mary recalls telling her instructor that one physician strongly objected to calling her Miss Booker. Rather, he called her Mammy or Mandy. Her instructor understood and Mary was not penalized for this breach of hospital etiquette. It was perhaps because of this unwelcome attention that Mary became a health advocate for the underserved. In Toledo in the 1950s, poor or African American patients were not given semi-private rooms. Rather, they were placed in wards or in the hallway. Mary remembers "I tried to make sure they had water, pain medication, back rubs and so on, just like the other patients. It was the way things were."

As a young girl, Mary did not stand out in her community. Her mother owned a business and both parents were well known. She was

---

[28]Darlene Clark Hine, "The Ethel Johns Report: Black Women in the Nursing Profession, 1925," *The Journal of Negro History* 67, no. 3 (1982).

[29]Sonya J. Grypma, "Profile of a Leader: Unearthing Ethel Johns's "Buried" Commitment to Racial Equality," *Nursing Leadership* 16, no. 4 (2003).

simply Mrs. Booker's daughter. It was not until she started working with the St. Vincent Hospital Health Promotion program that her community began to recognize her skills.

Her career had many highlights including charge nurse in surgery at St. Vincent Hospital, instructor at St. Vincent Hospital School of Nursing, and as the supervisor of the first surgical technician program in Ohio (1966). Mary was director of the federally funded St. Vincent Sickle Cell Project serving 11 counties (1974), and was appointed by Gov. Bob Taft to the Ohio Commission on Minority Health in 2006. She remained active in the Toledo Council of Black Nurses, serving as president in 1981.

From 1970 until her retirement in 1995, Mary served as manager of Health Promotion at St. Vincent Hospital. Through funding from the hospital and Channel 13, she had access to the Health Van. Populations who did not seek health care because of mistrust, access issues, and financial constraints were now served in the community. She addressed specific health problems of the African American population in Toledo, such as diabetes and hypertension. In her own words, Mary, and the Health Van "worked the streets." She differentiated "the streets" from "the community" because she went where the people who needed care lived. Mary offered screening clinics and health presentations in churches, migrant camps, and schools. She recalls people coming up to her in the grocery to tell her that they were following her teaching to watch their diets and take their medications, and they were thrilled to report when their blood pressure decreased. She is proud that she has been able to touch the lives of those who may have been missed.

Mary Gregory's career was interesting and diverse and was served entirely at St. Vincent Hospital. By her own admission, she realized that to some, she was a "token," but added, "those that I worked with and St. Vincent Hospital were always good to me."[30]

---

[30]Mary Booker Gregory, 2009.

In 1951, the year she graduated from nursing school, she married Raymond Gregory and they had four children. While working and raising a family, Mary earned a bachelor's degree in Education and a master's degree in Health Education and Administration from the University of Toledo. Among her many honors were an outstanding service award from N.A.A.C.P.; Woman of the Year, Ohio Chapter, Alpha Theta of Theta Nu Sigma; and the Professional Award from the National Association of Negro Business and Professional Women's Club.

As the first African American to graduate from nursing school in Toledo in 1951, Mary Booker Gregory made a difference. Education as preparation for entry into nursing school and the need for ongoing education has been her continuing message. Because of Mary's work, doors have been open for others to follow and the health of those who were underserved in Toledo has improved.

Sister Rita Mary Wasserman: A Graduate who Obeyed and Found Joy

Sister Rita Mary Wasserman did not choose nursing. "I believe what I am sharing will pertain to most religious communities. I am a Sister of Mercy and I came into the Community in 1946. Most people coming into a religious community did not say what they wanted to be or in what capacity they wanted to serve. We, as religious, accepted assignments to serve," she said.

Wasserman

Following her years of formation in the Novitiate, Sister was asked to be a teacher by the Mercy Community. She remembers, "I was to be sent to a teacher's college. But before registering for classes, I was informed that there was an emergency need for a teacher in Toledo. So, I simply went to the school and taught. After a year teaching in Toledo, I received a letter for my next year's assignment. I expected it to be for another year of teaching. Instead, it said that I was to train as a nurse at Mercy Hospital School of Nursing in Toledo. There was a need for registered nurses. My choice was to obey and accept the assignment. This is religious obedience and what is expected."

Sr. Rita Mary obeyed her calling as a religious Sister and became a registered nurse. She graduated from Mercy Hospital School of Nursing in 1952. In the 1940s and 1950s there were usually two or three Sisters in each nursing class. They lived in the convent with the other Sisters. Because she did not live in the nursing school dorms, Sr. Rita remembers being glad she was spared the initiation rites of other new students. As nursing student uniforms, the Sisters were required to wear their white habits while on clinicals.

Immediately upon graduation, Sister was assigned to be a nursing supervisor. She held supervisory positions for many years and eventually became the Director of Nursing for Mercy and St. Charles Hospitals in Toledo. Sr. Rita Mary received her bachelor's degree in 1954.

After nearly 30 years in nursing supervision and nursing administration, Sister was assigned to the St. Bernardine Home in Fremont to provide healthcare for retired Sisters. She took a break from healthcare administration and returned to direct, hands-on nursing care.

In 1982, she was asked to take on the role of Chief Executive Officer (CEO) at St. Rita's Hospital in Lima, Ohio, a position she held for six years. Despite her intensive work responsibilities, Sr. Rita Mary began graduate school part time to complete her master's degree in Administration from the University of Notre Dame.

St. Rita's Hospital experienced growth under Sr. Rita Mary's leadership. Many long-term projects were in the planning and early implementation phases during this time. When considering how to provide the best continuity at St. Rita's, Sister considered many factors. She knew that there would be continued development at the hospital and that because of her age, she would not see all projects through to completion. She sought and received permission to resign the CEO position.

In 1988, not wanting her talents to go to waste, the president of the Mercy Health Care System asked her to work in Willard, Ohio.[31] She remembers, "I can still see myself saying, where's Willard?" She did find out where Willard was and spent the next 25 years there as assistant administrator responsible for Human Resources, Environmental Services, Volunteers, Materials Management and Dietary. It was here "my life touched many people."

In 1993, a pastoral care position opened at Mercy Willard Hospital. This work became the focus of her ministry and the joy of her life. She took a course in Clinical Pastoral Education (CPE), which taught her the skills needed in hospital chaplaincy. She joined the ministerial association and began outreach to the other small communities surrounding Willard, such as Plymouth, Greenwich, New Washington. "It was so rich to know them and to be able to reach out to them when their people were patients at the hospital." [32] Pastors would call her when their members were in the hospital. She visited families at times of tragedy, times of stress, and times of joy. Doctors would call her to follow up with patients at home with phone calls or visits just to make sure everything was going well. She attended services at almost every church of every denomination in the area for funerals, weddings, holiday services, and baptisms. The Mennonite and Amish communities were not closely involved with the health care system. Through Sister Rita Mary's work with members of the Mennonite community, trust developed and made it possible for her to reach out in friendship to the Amish community. Through her efforts, many Mennonite and Amish have been helped with needed access to healthcare in the area.

---

[31] News Editor Jane Ernsberger, "A Life of Service in a Life Filled with Mercy: Sister Rita Mary Wasserman Celebrates 70 Years in Religious Life, Part 1," *Willard Times-Junction*, 9/19/2016 2016.

[32] "A Life of Service Filled with Mercy: Sister Rita Mary Wasserman Celebrates 70 Years in Religious Life (Part 2)," ibid.

During her time at Mercy Hospital Willard, she also found time to be actively involved as Mercy Hospital School of Nursing transitioned from a diploma school of nursing to a college granting associate, baccalaureate and master degrees in nursing as well as degrees in other related health care professions. Through service as a board member, Sister helped guide the development of Mercy College of Ohio.

Sr. Rita Mary has spread the message of the Roman Catholic Church through the Sisters of Mercy for over 70 years in her healthcare and community involvement. She is recognized for the compassion and care she has brought to Willard. A meeting room in the new Mercy Willard Hospital has recently been named in her honor.

Sr. Rita Mary Wasserman's willingness to serve and obedience to meeting the needs of the religious and lay communities have benefitted countless individuals and families in northwest Ohio. Although she initially thought her path would lead to teaching, it was in nursing that she has found her greatest joy. Her diploma education and devotion to the Mercy Sisters provided her with the gifts she needed to minister to the people she has touched.

Carol Manley Singer: On the Forefront of Advance Practice Nursing

Singer

"It seems that I've always come in the back door in my career," said Carol Manley Singer. "I didn't often plan very far in advance." Following graduation from Holland High School (now Springfield High School), Carol could not decide what to do. Her grandmother owned a nursing home and during summer breaks, Carol had worked there. It was not like nursing homes today, she recalls. They were called "rest homes." A LPN who worked at the home impressed Carol. She seemed to know what to do to keep patient care running smoothly. Additionally, Carol had two friends who, a year before, applied to Toledo Hospital School of Nursing. One was admitted and the other was not. Her secret dream career was to become a physician. "Elizabeth Blackwell was my hero," she remembers. Becoming a physician was a far-fetched dream for a young woman in the 1950s. She also knew that her parents could not afford college, much less medical school.

In July 1958, armed with a desire to heal, a nursing role model, and a friend to lead the way, Carol called Toledo Hospital School of Nursing and spoke to the director. She was told that admissions were closed but she could apply to another school in Toledo, or she could apply again next year. This did not deter her. She remembers, "I told the director that Toledo Hospital School of Nursing was the best school and the only school I wanted to attend." The director relented and agreed to have the admissions committee review her application if Carol could arrange for submission of all required academic records, register at the University of Toledo, and complete all health exams, immunizations, and psychological testing by the admission deadline. Carol completed all requirements, was interviewed by the director, and admitted to the Toledo Hospital School of Nursing, Class of 1961. To defray expenses, she received a loan from Toledo Hospital Women's Auxiliary Student Nurse Fund. The loan was interest free for the first six months after graduation. Carol needed to borrow all tuition expenses. For the three-year program, the total amount was $695.00. She is proud to say that she paid it back interest free.

Carol adapted well to nursing school and enjoyed the work. She remembers the strict rules. "They owned us" she said. "We had eight late passes each month. We signed in and out of the dorm. They told us what to wear and how to behave. Breaking rules resulted in grounding or even dismissal. It never occurred to us to question the authority of the school. If we behaved in a manner that was considered inappropriate, consequences would follow." Carol recalled a group of student nurses who, as a prank, threw water balloons at another group of students from the roof top porch at the dorm. The response was swift and severe. The students who played the prank were grounded to the dorm for one month. "In those times, it was expected that nurses knew their place. Nursing wasn't really considered a highly-regarded profession then in Toledo. A lot of it had to do with nursing as a woman's work. Doctors were men and men were considered more important than women."

The art of nursing has always been important to Carol. "The entire first year, many of our classes were called Nursing Arts. It gave us the skills to provide physical and supportive care to patients. I remembered those foundations every time I cared for patients." Clinical experience at Toledo Hospital School of Nursing was entirely hospital based, although community agencies were visited from time to time. Patient care responsibilities came early. "During the first semester of my second year, I affiliated with Cincinnati Children's Hospital for our pediatric nursing rotation. Because Toledo Hospital School of Nursing was considered one of the best schools, we were sometimes in charge of entire nursing units at Children's," she recalls. "By our third year, we were often in charge of nursing units at Toledo Hospital on the 3 p.m. to 11 p.m. shift at the hospital. When I think about how much we were expected to know and do so early in our education, it is astonishing."

Following graduation and becoming a registered nurse, Carol went to work in a nursing home her family had opened. She remembers that her task was to set up and organize the systems of nursing care for the facility. She enjoyed the work of getting the nursing home off the ground, and was grateful for the organizational skills she learned at Toledo Hospital School of Nursing. She then returned to hospital work on an orthopedic unit at St. Vincent Hospital.

Although Carol remembers that most of her peers did not see the need for further education, she did. It would be another 12 years before a bachelor of science in nursing program would open in Toledo. In 1962, Carol attended Bowling Green State University and eventually the University of Toledo to earn a bachelor's degree. Because she had completed some course work beyond a diploma, in 1969, the director of St. Vincent Hospital School of Nursing hired her as a clinical instructor. Diploma programs continued to be the mainstay of nursing education in the region. Carol remembers, "I read the American Nurses Association White Paper recommending a BSN as the entry level for professional nursing practice. I did understand its implications, but at the time (49 years ago), I couldn't imagine how it could happen. Diploma nurses were simply the best prepared. I do recall, though, that the reaction from the Toledo nursing community was nuclear!"

Through contact with colleagues, she heard about a program for nurse anesthetists at St. Vincent Hospital. This program was a unique opportunity to earn the education and eventual certification to become an advance practice nurse. An advance practice nurse is a person with specialty nursing education beyond a basic nursing program and is certified by a nationally recognized professional nursing organization. The state board of nursing determines which national organizations are acceptable to certify advance practice nurses in the state. In the early 1970s, advance practice nurses were unusual. This was especially true in Toledo.

The nurse anesthetist program at St. Vincent only accepted four students in each class and admissions were competitive. To quality for admission, each candidate had to have critical care nursing experience. Carol had no critical care experience, so she left teaching and began to work in the adult Intensive Care Unit. "I was so intimidated. The content was information I'd never learned in school. While we were learning about electrolytes balance, I remember going back to one of my nursing textbooks. There were two pages on electrolytes. Why didn't we learn this important information?" she wondered. In the 14 years since she had graduated from Toledo Hospital School of Nursing, medical and nursing knowledge had exploded. Carol worked in the ICU when an opening became available in the nurse anesthetist program. "Once again, I was coming through the back door. The program had started six weeks earlier and one candidate suddenly dropped out. I was offered the opportunity. With support of the anesthesia faculty and very dedicated study, I was able to catch up." The nurses working in the operating rooms were supportive of the nurse anesthetist students. Carol recalls, "There was extreme prejudice, though, from non-nurses in the surgical area. The pervasive attitude was that doctors were more capable to give anesthesia, not nurses. In fact, until I experienced the educational requirements and collegiality with physicians, I must admit I was one of those biased people."

In 1974, Carol completed both the nurse anesthetist program and a Bachelor of Education in Community Affairs and Public Service from the University of Toledo. She passed national boards and became a Certified Registered Nurse Anesthetist (CRNA). Throughout a career that spanned more than 40 years, Carol Singer was on the forefront of many advancements in CRNA practice. She found her niche in obstetrics, a natural fit. She could have contact with awake and alert patients while practicing OB anesthesia. In 1979, she became one of four OB CRNAs at Christ Hospital in Cincinnati. Regional anesthesia was a new area of practice for many CRNAs. Carol promoted, and received, training in epidural blocks at the University of Cincinnati. Once an epidural is given, women can experience nearly pain free labor. At least five years before physicians in Toledo offered such care, Carol and her team of CRNAs provided epidural anesthesia around the clock for laboring women at Christ Hospital.

"At the end of my training at the university, the OB anesthesiologist asked if I had questions. Then he said, 'Of course you don't. You've only done 50 epidurals. When you have done 500, then you'll know what to ask.' I never forgot that knowledge is needed, but experience is essential. He was right. I needed to do many more epidurals before I became truly proficient." Shortly after, she was officially appointed Chief OB CRNA at Christ Hospital.

When asked to describe the accomplishment of which she is most proud as a CRNA, she was humble. "It was never just me. All other OB CRNAs on our team shared the same high standards. Each member was uniquely and equally part of the standards we developed and maintained, and the care we provided."

Singer was Chief CRNA in OB at Christ Hospital, Cincinnati for 25 years. She retired in 2014 but not before transitioning the Chief OB CRNA responsibilities to her successor.

Upon reflection, Carol is astonished at the changes in nursing over the last half century. She believes that nursing, more than any other profession, has matured to benefit careers for women. The advancements in collegiate and graduate nursing education, particularly in advance practice nursing, have her full support. The explosion of nursing knowledge and technology advances are probably the most significant changes she has seen. These changes have the potential to make care safer. Yet, Carol makes a point to emphasize that with the benefits of technology comes the nurse's responsibility to remember the patient, not the machine, is the focus of nursing care. "Nurses are most effective if they use their senses, as well as technology to assess patients. It isn't possible to simply learn the technology and the classroom content and then expect to safely care for patients. My anesthesia mentor was right. You need experience to become competent. Sometimes it really does take 500 times."

Carol Manley Singer may have come to nursing and CRNA practice "through the back door," but she is a role model for advance practice nursing. Her diploma education provided the basis for the advance practice of providing individualized pain relief and anesthesia for laboring obstetric patients. A book dedication written to her at her retirement from a colleague sums up the respect Carol enjoyed as a CRNA, advance practice nurse. "For what you have done for our group, for what you have done for our profession, for what you have done for me, thank you, live long, rest well and a job well done."

Elaine Studer Hetherwick: A Graduate who Blended Entrepreneur and Administrator Paths

Hetherwick

Elaine Studer did not plan to become a nurse. In high school, she took secretarial courses and no science classes. She was told she was "smarter" than that. Two mothers of friends encouraged her to consider nursing. So, Elaine took the entrance exam to become a Licensed Practical Nurse. She scored "too high" on the test and was denied admission. She applied at Maumee Valley Hospital School of Nursing and was again denied admission. "I had never taken a high school level science course other than general science. I didn't have any credentials." For some reason, Elaine decided that she would prove she could get into nursing school. So, she took the required science courses and was admitted the following year.

The academic college and nursing courses were enjoyable, but Elaine was not sure she could really be a nurse. "I fainted during admission lab work the first week of school!" However, her freshman instructor was supportive. Once she accomplished her first injection, Elaine says, "I kind of got over that."

"I loved nursing," she recalls. "I couldn't believe I could be paid to do this work. I didn't even think about the money. To me, it really was a higher calling."

Elaine embraced traditional nursing symbols. "Everyone had a different cap. We all wore them. No discussion. It was the way we were identified as a RN in the hospital. Our Maumee Valley cap was very fancy with lots of pleats. I never did get the hang of folding it properly."

During her senior year, an instructor told Elaine, "you'll never be a leader." She recalls, "This made me so mad, that I went to work in the Intensive Care Unit right after graduation in 1966." Hospital nursing care was different in the mid-1960s, and Intensive Care Units were a brand-new concept. Patients with myocardial infarctions (heart attacks) were moved out of the wards and into a special new Coronary Care Unit. Premature babies often died from respiratory distress syndrome because artificial surfactant had not been developed. Elaine remembers that not much was known about how to support critically ill patients "We improvised…a lot."

Elaine wanted to go back to school. Maumee Valley Hospital was part of the Medical College of Ohio at Toledo (now the University of Toledo.) When they started a BSN program in the early 1970s, Elaine applied. "The director told me I would need to start all over, except for the courses I had taken at Mary Manse College. She told me 'We are not a retread for diploma nurses.' I gave up on the idea of a degree for many years."

Elaine's nursing career took her from critical care staff nursing at Maumee Valley to nursing supervision at St. Luke's Hospital. Then, Elaine married a man with an entrepreneurial spirit…and things changed. She and her husband opened a children's apparel store in the trendy Portside in downtown Toledo. They opened stores that were well known in Toledo for being "the place" to get all things Buckeye and Wolverine. Elaine's ability to improvise translated into business success. But, she missed health care.

Elaine became interested in geriatric nursing. She was a director of nursing at large nursing homes for a number of years, and then obtained a nursing home administrator's license. Because a BSN degree was hard to obtain at the time, Elaine designed her own curriculum and earned a Bachelor of Independent Studies.

Today, Elaine is past the traditional age of retirement. She remains committed to excellent patient care for older adults living in nursing facilities and serves as an administrator and consultant for a large nursing home chain in the Toledo area.

Elaine Studer Hetherwick has never let an opportunity go by without evaluating it. Over the past 50 years, her leadership skills and commitment to excellence led from the secretarial pool to critical care nurse and manager to small business owner and to nursing home administrator.

Catherine Van Vorce Horner: A Graduate who Followed a Non-traditional Career Path to Become a Physician

Cathy Van Vorce Horner's original career goals did not include medical school. When she was seven years old, Cathy had a tonsillectomy. Two days' post operatively, she developed appendicitis and had an appendectomy. This unusual set of circumstances lead to a one week stay in the hospital. This was in the days before appropriate play and diversion for hospitalized pediatric patients. To occupy her active child's mind, the nurses allowed

Horner

Cathy to sit in and nurses' station and help put papers in the charts. Cathy remembers this was "very cool" and so decided to become a nurse.

She laughed as she recalled how little she knew of admission requirements, and was dismayed to learn that her grade point average was too low to get into nursing school. "I loved to read, just not textbooks." She studied hard her last two years of high school and was accepted into Flower Hospital School of Nursing. She enjoyed nursing school, especially the science courses taken at the University of Toledo.

Cathy's recollection of nursing school reflects both the times and her focus on excellent patient care. "It was the 1960s, the era of the mini skirt. Our uniforms had to be mid-calf....When the doctors entered the nurses' station, we nurses stood up. I didn't think that was odd. It was the way it was. Doctors were considered superior to nurses...We were assigned large numbers of patients, but individual patient needs were always emphasized by the instructors."

Cathy was a pragmatic student. "One of my instructors was former military. She was a tough bird and sent me off clinicals once for shoes that weren't polished well enough. I purchased shoes that didn't need to be polished. Even though they made my feet smell, I wasn't sent off clinicals again."

Cathy understood the importance of tradition. "I remember the capping ceremony. It was a big deal. We said the Nightingale Pledge and had lit ceramic lamps. Since we were no longer probies, we could wear the full student uniform. I felt like a real nurse after getting the cap."

Cathy participated fully in the dorm life of the student nurse. "Your classmates were your family. Curfews were strict. We dated but it was restricted. Friends would leave the laundry room window unlocked so that other girls could climb in after curfew. That was great until the house mother figured it out." (She is quick to clarify that she never did this. "I was the straight- laced type.")

Nursing school was not easy academically. "We lost one third of our class the first semester." She did well and graduated in 1969, passed State Boards and began working as a staff nurse at Flower Hospital.

About three months after graduation, Cathy decided to go back to school to become "maybe a nurse midwife or work in public health." "I knew I needed a bachelor's degree in nursing."

That is when she found out just how difficult it was in the 1960s and 1970s to earn a BSN after earning a diploma. "I was told I would have to start at the beginning, except for the few science courses I had from the university. There was no BSN program in the area. Even if I moved, I would have had to retake all nursing courses. That made me feel so frustrated. So, I decided to go to medical school." She earned a bachelor's degree in psychology and took the additional 30 credit hours of sciences required and applied to medical school. She was accepted at the Medical College of Ohio at Toledo (now the University of Toledo College of Medicine.)

Her skills as a RN allowed her to work weekends all through college and until the second year of medical school. "Nursing allowed me a perspective that my medical school classmates didn't have. Things like understanding medical terminology and familiarity with commonly prescribed treatments were obvious. "Gross" things were not shocking and hospital routines were comfortable, not foreign. Yet, some of the most important skills I needed to know as a physician, I first learned as a nurse. I was comfortable talking to patients. Touching and examining patients was not threatening to me. This was essential. I understood how to adapt teaching to their level of knowledge. My ability to empathize was well developed at Flower Hospital School of Nursing and continues to affect the way I approach my patients."

Upon graduation from medical school, Cathy completed a three-year family practice residency. She worked on a Navajo reservation for one year and then joined the military. Her assignments took her around the world. She married and started a family. Cathy remained active duty for four years, worked as a civilian doctor in the Air Force for five years, and then entered private practice. In 2016, Dr. Catherine Van Vorce Horner retired from active practice. She continues to volunteer time and medical skills at a free clinic near her central Florida retirement home, and is a member of the Florida State Medical Emergency Response Team.

Dr. Horner ruefully acknowledges that she may have chosen the more difficult path when the university refused to acknowledge the academic worth of her nursing diploma. Yet, the blend of nursing and medicine gave her a perspective that patients have found invaluable for four decades. "I am able to look beyond the diagnosis and treatment of disease and see the effects of illness and prevention on patients' lives. That, to me, is quality patient care."

Diane Knoblauch: A Graduate who Blended Nurse Practitioner and Attorney Practices

It started out as a good choice to assure an income source. Diane Knoblauch was engaged to be married and wanted to continue her education. She was practical though, and wanted to have a well-paying career when finished. Following in her mother's footsteps (Mary Keefer McCaskey, Toledo Hospital School of Nursing, Class of 1952), Diane entered nursing school.

Knoblauch

She appreciates the education and experiences from the Toledo Hospital School of Nursing. "The Tuesday afternoon teas were such a nice tradition. They showed respect for our caring work and respect for the lovely parts of life." Ceremonies, such as capping and lamp lighting, were meaningful. "Our milestones were heavy with legacy; it is our responsibility to carry the torch." Embracing the nursing tradition, Diane believes she has a responsibility to make life better for individuals and the community.

Diane excelled in nursing school. She especially enjoyed clinicals. One experience is clearly remembered. "It was my first clinical experience, with my first patient. All my skill checklists were up to date. I was assigned a post-operative patient with a radiation implant following extensive and radical surgery for cancer. She was in isolation because of the radiation therapy. While checking vital signs, I saw that she needed some important physical care that had been left undone for some time. My instructor helped me with this somewhat complicated care and made certain I understood the patient's care needs. That incident shaped a value and commitment to patient dignity that I practice to this day."

Following graduation in 1976, Diane worked in an adult intensive care unit and returned to school, earning a BSN in 1978. Wanting more professional autonomy, she entered a graduate nursing program. In 1980, she was awarded a Master of Science in Nursing in adult nursing with a minor in administration. She successfully completed testing for adult nurse practitioner certification. Her work as a nurse practitioner took her from a physician's office and hospital practice to outreach in the poorest neighborhoods in the community. She was led to occupational health at a nuclear power plant where she provided care for employees and consulted with businesses in manufacturing and energy production. "Although I could practice with increasing autonomy in clinical judgment and flexible critical thinking skills, I was exposed to legal issues in occupational health. I was bitten by the legal bug; I needed more knowledge and a different set of skills."

In 1990, Diane entered law school, part-time, while working as an assistant professor teaching undergraduate and graduate nursing students. In addition, she worked two to three weekends per month in a surgical intensive care unit, and raised three children. "I didn't sleep much," she recalls. Following graduation from law school in 1993, she passed the bar exam and began blending a law practice with advanced nursing practice. Diane is now licensed as an attorney in two states. She has a general civil practice and specializes in assisting nurses in disciplinary matters before the State Board of Nursing. She still works every week in the surgical intensive care unit caring for patients at the bedside. "Of course, it is hard work," she says, "but it is time away from my law practice to care for my patients. Clinical practice is an important part of who I am, advocating for patients and their families and making a real difference, one patient and one family at a time.

Diane has authored book chapters establishing standards of practice for occupational health nurses and frequently lectures on nursing legal and ethical issues.

"A lot has changed in nursing since 1976," Diane says. "Collegiality between physicians and nurses has greatly improved. We work together much more collegially than when I graduated from Toledo Hospital School of Nursing. Knowing how things work within both the health care delivery system and the law helps me with both of my practices. I identify myself as a nurse-attorney. It's important to me that the 'nurse' is first. I am committed to helping my nursing colleagues practice safely within the requirements of regulatory agencies. As nurses, we are held to a high standard of practice; our patients trust us."

Diane Knoblauch is a strong advocate for nurses and patients. "I have been very lucky to have great nursing mentors. Each one influenced who I am as a nurse; they encouraged me to do something different, to be on the forefront of health care cost containment; to step outside my comfort zone and grow personally and professionally. As a professional, opportunities are presented to us. We have to be willing to embrace them, to take a chance and trust our judgement to make a positive change."

Sharon Bee: A Graduate who Followed a Traditional Career Path

Sharon Bee, like many diploma nursing school graduates, values education. A member of the Toledo Hospital School of Nursing, class of 1977, she is quick to say that learning has never stopped for her, whether in her basic program or after attaining RN licensure.

Sharon's entry into nursing was influenced by a family illness. While helping care for her hospitalized grandmother, she observed nurses who knew how to help. **Bee**

Sharon always enjoyed studying the sciences. Nursing seemed like a good fit for her. She withdrew from a college where her major was physical education, and applied to and was accepted at Toledo Hospital School of Nursing. Sharon started toward her goal of becoming a RN, and never looked back. This was the first, but not the last time her career path moved in an unexpected direction. Her advice to other nurses, and those considering nursing, is, "Professional obstacles seem to always come up. Stay flexible and open to possibilities."

Her purposeful and flexible career path included going back to school within three years of graduation from nursing school. Since she had already taken college courses both at Adrian College and at the University of Toledo as part of Toledo Hospital School of Nursing's curriculum, she was not intimidated about more schooling. Education has always been a way to increased professional autonomy for Sharon.

Sharon's career has been traditional, with some modern twists. Her one unchanging career focus has been on providing the best care possible, particularly for children.

Following graduation, she worked at Riverside Hospital as a staff nurse, charge nurse, and nurse manager in pediatrics. Participation in hospital committee work widened her perspective of health care. After 18 years, Sharon felt the need to improve her technical skills working with sick children. She changed hospitals and worked in the Pediatric Intensive Care Unit at the Medical College of Ohio Hospital. Continuing to practice her philosophy of "always learning," Sharon returned to school again while working in the Pediatric ICU. She earned a Bachelor of Science in Nursing and maintained her professional certification as a pediatric nurse. Soon, an opportunity to provide continuing education to nurses presented itself, and she moved again, this time to St. Vincent Medical Center (now Mercy St. Vincent Medical Center.) Sharon found that she loves nursing education. The satisfaction of watching nurses grow professionally and measuring the patient benefits is gratifying.

Sharon's openness to new possibilities in nursing is anything but traditional. When the new and evolving field of Nursing Informatics (NI) opened in Toledo, Sharon was there. Technology is ubiquitous in health care. The amount of health information available, the number of providers who need this information, and the challenges of patient privacy has made it vital for the nurse to skillfully utilize this technology. The Healthcare Information and Management Systems Society (HIMSS), a global network of health information technology professionals states that "NI is the specialty that integrates nursing science with multiple information management and analytical sciences to identify, define, manage, and communicate data, information, knowledge, and wisdom in nursing practice. NI supports nurses, consumers, patients, the inter-professional healthcare team, and other stakeholders in their decision-making in all roles and settings to achieve desired outcomes. This support is accomplished using information structures, information processes, and information technology." [33] Sharon enjoyed working in Nursing

[33] Health Care Information Management Society, "Health Care Information Management Systems Society." 2016.

Informatics throughout the Mercy system, teaching and encouraging nurses to make health care technology work for them. Sharon's calm reinforcement was an important reason nurses began to embrace the electronic health record. Sharon believes that helping nurses utilize this technology is improving patient care throughout our community.

The nursing students at Mercy College of Ohio are now benefitting from Sharon's knowledge and experience in nursing of children and health care information management. She is an assistant professor in the Associate Degree in Nursing program at the college. Her advice to students shows a deep understanding of professional nursing. "Keep your eyes and minds open. Stay involved. There are always exciting new opportunities in professional nursing practice."

Jeff Lycan: A Graduate with Statewide Influence

Jeff Lycan has dedicated his career to making a difference to some of the most vulnerable patients and their families. Jeff has worked for decades on behalf of those with life threatening illnesses and those who are dying. In his current role as President of Ohio's Hospice Alliance, he represents 20 nonprofit hospices that care for 42 percent of those who die under hospice care in Ohio.

Lycan

Working with legislators and others who influence state policy, his results are not always noticed. Through advocacy and lobbying, Jeff is directly involved in shaping a health care environment which comforts, respects, and supports patients at the end of life. Every day his commitment to palliative care and hospice is felt in Ohio.

This career track did not happen in a vacuum. Looking back on his education at Toledo Hospital School of Nursing, Jeff says he has always been a "hands on" learner. That may be the primary reason a diploma nursing school education was the perfect fit for him. Drawn to the healing professions while he was working as an orderly at Toledo Hospital, he decided to apply to its diploma nursing school. He was accepted.

Jeff was a nontraditional student in a traditional program. He was a male, in his twenties, was married, lived in an apartment with his wife, and had a variety of work experiences both in and out of health care. While in nursing school, he continued to work at least 24 hours per week as an orderly. He was an independent student with adult expenses and needed the money.

Jeff recalls from his early experiences as an orderly that he was one of the few who did not mind transporting a body to the morgue. He strongly felt the need for dignity and respect in this last task for the patient. Perhaps he thought he could do this last duty best. This was particularly true if the deceased was a newborn. Respect at the end of life was his passion.

Despite these differences from his more traditional classmates, he flourished in nursing school. Jeff was a leader. In an overwhelmingly female student body, Jeff was voted president of the Student Nurses Organization. Even his wife Karen was a little incredulous, "Why are they electing you over a female?" he recalls her asking. Over 30 years later, Jeff laughs and says that question remains unanswered. Internally motivated to succeed, he felt strongly that "this is where I belong." After graduation, his leadership skills continued to grow.

Jeff graduated in 1984, during one of the periodic cycles of a nursing supply excess in the Toledo area, and few jobs were available for a new RN. He first found employment as a new graduate on an oncology unit in Columbus, Ohio. But his desire was to work in a research oriented medical center on the bone marrow transplant unit at The Ohio State University's James Cancer Hospital. Within a year, he achieved this goal and began a 14 year tenure at Ohio State.

As a new nurse, Jeff worked the afternoon and night shifts. This gave him an opportunity to learn more about how the state legislature affects health care. During off hours, he would read briefs and sit in on hearings. He was fascinated with how politics can affect the quality of health care in the state. Throughout his career, Jeff has influenced political change, whether the political change was organizational or governmental. Early in his career, he was a board member of the Ohio Nurses Association, and safe staffing and bedside nurse representation in patient care decisions were his focus. He worked on the Certificate of Needs laws in Ohio and the original Advance Practice Nursing bill. During his employment at Ohio State, Jeff returned to school to complete a bachelor's degree in the Management of Nursing Services. Soon after, he applied for the role of nurse manager on an oncology critical care unit in the hospital. As his career moved him away from the bedside, he wondered whether he would still have an impact on direct patient care. He soon realized that the patient would continue to be the center of his work.

Jeff's first job interview for a position outside the hospital setting was for executive director of the Ohio Hospice and Palliative Care Organization (OHPCO). He wondered how he could be effective with only inpatient experience as the board members interviewing him likely wondered this as well. During the interview, he told them two stories about how he had influenced end-of-life care.

There was a young Indian boy dying after his cancer relapsed. He was a patient on the transplant unit where Jeff worked. It was clear he would not make it home; he would die in the hospital setting. In this young man's culture, it was required that he die on the ground so that he could reach eternal rest. How could this belief be honored in this highly medical setting? With Jeff's input, he and his colleagues devised a plan that bent most hospital rules about patient safety and infection control. This young man was tenderly placed on the floor with his family around him. The patient and his family's needs were respected.

Another patient, about Jeff's age, was in the transplant unit. It was a tough case, and the patient's treatment was failing and he was going to die. Jeff recalls when walking in the room to care for him, the patient said, "I thought I would get one of the pretty nurses." Jeff's laughing response and calm demeanor quickly sealed a trusting nurse-patient relationship. Jeff attended this man's funeral and remembered how the family warmly greeted him and escorted him into the receiving line to meet others who had gathered. He clearly understood then that nurses not only have impact on the patient, but also on those family and friends. Most nurses may never meet these people, but nursing's indirect influence can still be powerful and strong. He has never forgotten that.

Jeff was given the job as executive director and led OHPCO, a position he held for 17 years. One of Jeff's most prized moments in his professional career was as a recipient of the American Cancer Society National Lane Adams Quality of Life Award in 2006. Jeff realizes that success is seeing the intended impact of one's efforts, whether providing care at the bedside or creating policy. "When we provide dignity and respect in our care for another, whether the outcome is living or dying, the privilege to serve others and helping achieve their personal health goals, is what nursing is all about." Today he works in advocacy around the state of Ohio through the Hospice Alliance. Although he has continued his education, earning bachelor's and master's degrees, it was his fundamental education at Toledo Hospital School of Nursing that launched this career. It is a career that continues to influence compassionate care of the dying in Ohio.

Kaye Lani Rae Rafko Wilson: A Graduate with National Influence

Kaye Lani Rae Rafko's journey to becoming Miss America 1988 started with the need for nursing school tuition money. A Search for Values course taken in high school followed by many service hours as a candy striper in her local hospital was enough to convince her she wanted a career in nursing. She was accepted at St. Vincent Hospital School of Nursing. The summer before classes were to begin, she realized that she was short $750 in tuition money

Wilson

for the courses to be taken at Lourdes College. Her friend told her, "The Miss Monroe County prize is $750. You can dance, why not enter?" Kaye Lani entered, won, and had tuition money for nursing school. She continued to enter contests...and win. Nursing school also continued and she graduated in 1985 and passed NCLEX. She had a great job on the oncology unit at St. Vincent Hospital.

She was first runner up for Miss Michigan and then decided to stop. "I was working nights at the hospital and had never been a model, so the pageant commitments during the day were becoming burdensome. I decided to quit the pageant life and focus on my career in nursing," she said. One of her patients would not let her stop. "Try again for Miss Michigan. You can win," she encouraged. Kaye Lani was not easily convinced.

Kaye Lani truly enjoyed nursing. While other student nurses were complaining about all the work involved in preparing for clinicals, Kaye Lani did not. "I loved having my own patient. When reading up the night before clinicals, they became more than a diagnosis or room number— they became real people."

Nursing school was not easy, but gave her a sense of accomplishment. She graduated in 1985. "I had to get it right, because patients depended on me. Nurses are very often the piece of the patient care wheel that keeps everything moving."

In 1987, Kaye Lani decided to try the Miss Michigan pageant once again. She won and went on to win the Miss America title in 1988. "I went from the night nurse on 3A to the Miss America Organization. It was so different."

Kaye Lani remembers that her colleagues, as a bit of teasing, put up one of her pageant pictures in the nurses' station. "I had my hair done up, make up expertly applied and a very posed smile. While making rounds, one of the oncologists looked at the picture and said, 'Who is that?' I replied, 'It's me.' He looked at me and then the picture and back again. 'You never come here looking like that,' he said. He was a little embarrassed. I still laugh about his reaction. There I stood in my scrubs with hair pulled back into a pony tail, my pockets full of papers and pens and wearing a stethoscope. That is a very long way from Miss Michigan!"

In 1988, the Miss America pageant did not require a platform or cause to support during the winner's reigning year, and it was not particularly noteworthy that Miss America was a nurse. In Portland, Maine, Kaye Lani found herself (with her Miss America chaperone) at a gathering with 5,000 people who had come to get her autograph. The master of ceremonies ran late. The crowd became restless. The chaperone suggested that Kaye Lani stand up and say a few words. "I didn't know what to say. She told me to tell them a little bit about myself. So, I spoke about nursing and care of patients with cancer. I described my dream to work with hospice someday. I was able to share what I love and what was important to me." The response was immediate and overwhelming. Kaye Lani, Miss America The Nurse, became widely recognized. Speaking requests poured in. She was interviewed in the October 1987 issue of *People* magazine and was quoted in the *American Journal of Nursing*.

"I began to realize that people had no idea what nurses did. This was a wonderful opportunity to explain why men and women ought to consider nursing school." Not everyone was pleased with this attention. "I received letters from several nurse executives throughout our country," she remembers, who believed "nurses were thought of as handmaidens to physicians and not taken seriously as educated healthcare providers. They felt that associating nursing with any pageant would be taking a step backward. They actually asked me not to speak so openly about my career as I traveled that year as Miss America." Although taken aback at first, Kaye Lani's presentations about nursing continued. Her communication and public speaking skills were honed by the many resources within the Miss America Organization. The full impact of Kaye Lani's platform was not realized until after the year finished. She is proud to report that one of those nursing executives sent a later letter apologizing and admitting that she made an error in judgement.

Today, Kaye Lani Rae Rafko Wilson lives in her small home town in Michigan. She is married and has raised a family. Her dream of working with patients and families who are grieving has been achieved. As Director of Gabby's Ladder, she and her staff provide bereavement counseling and support to children and adults who have lost a loved one to death. Grants and active community support fund the program, and there is no charge for their services. She also co-hosts a local TV show with a fellow nurse. "All that I did as Miss America," she reflects, "it can't come close to what I did on 3A and continue to do today. Nursing is truly my ministry."

KEEPING THE STORY ALIVE

The story of diploma nursing education in Toledo is a rich one. Nearly 20 years after the last diploma program closed, countless graduates continue to contribute to the health care of patients around the world.

Diploma nursing school graduates are a committed group of professionals. For those who agreed to be interviewed for this book, thank you. For the many other Toledo diploma nurses who have provided encouragement, enthusiasm, and insightful quotes, please know this book could not have been completed without you. You have helped keep the story alive of diploma nursing education in Toledo. Your remembrances of the various paths and reasons you became a nurse, your delight in sharing your memories of living, learning, practicing, and acting like a nurse made this history relevant to twenty-first century professional nursing. Some nurses remembered entering nursing school with a compassionate intent, some became nurses because it was one of the only professions open to women at the time, and for some, the decision to become a nurse was purely a financial one. Regardless of motivation, all spoke about the privilege of being part of people's lives during the saddest, most frightening, as well as the most joyous times of life. Whether the nurse practiced for over 60 consecutive years (Mary Keefer McCaskey Toledo Hospital School of Nursing, Class of 1952) or stopped working as a nurse after a short time in practice (Hope J. Wyse Renton, Maumee Valley Hospital School of Nursing, Class of 1968), each Toledo diploma nurse interviewed was quick to remind us that every person is worthy of respect, quality health care is human right, and high standards are the key to quality nursing care.

Times have dramatically changed in health care since the late-nineteenth century.

Some important things stay the same, though.

"All my patients had dreams. I never forgot that."

Alice Miller
Toledo Hospital School of Nursing, Class of 1941

*"My patients give me as much as I give them. As I help them take care
of their health problems, they show me what it means to be a nurse. I still
consider patients' needs first."*

Norma Provencher Lake
St. Vincent Hospital School of Nursing, Class of 1974

*"The pregnant women I care for are vulnerable and need
compassionate support. That's what keeps me in nursing."*

Suzanne Mary Alexander Owen
St. Vincent Hospital School of Nursing, Class of 1974

*"No matter where I've practiced or how much education I receive, I've
never forgotten the definition of empathy I learned in nursing school 'Your
pain in my heart.'"*

Linda Lucas Graver
Toledo Hospital School of Nursing, Class of 1984

*"Nurses don't take care of bed numbers or diseases, we take care of
people. My patients didn't choose to be in the hospital. I did. That changes
my attitude and reminds me why I am there."*

Kaye Lani Rae Rafko Wilson
St. Vincent Hospital School of Nursing, Class of 1985

"Even in pre-HIPAA days, patient privacy was constantly stressed.
We never talked about patients outside the clinical setting. The patient's
privacy was part of putting the patient first. I always remember that."*

Lissa Wilhelm Brehm
St. Vincent Hospital School of Nursing, Class of 1995
**(Health Insurance Portability and Accountability Act,
the national patient information privacy law)*

Diploma nursing graduates in Toledo laid the foundation for the
collegiate based nursing education that is found today in northwest
Ohio and around the world. These diploma nurses are remembered and
honored.

"No system can endure that does not march. Are we walking to the future or the past? Are we progressing or are we stereotyping? We remember that we have barely crossed the threshold of uncivilized civilization in nursing: there is so much still to do."

– Florence Nightingale

Author Bios

Patricia Ringos Beach, a Clinical Nurse Specialist and Patient Navigator for the Mercy Health Cancer Program holds advanced certification in oncology and palliative care nursing. She watched with interest when her daughter Stacie went to nursing school, more than 30 years after she herself had received a diploma in nursing from St. Elizabeth Hospital School of Nursing in Youngstown, Ohio.

Beach

Although Patti later went on to receive a BSN from Capital University in Columbus, and a MSN from Medical College of Ohio at Toledo, she considers her diploma nursing education as "when she became a nurse." She could relate to Stacie's enthusiasm for nursing and to what she was learning in her BSN program but it became increasingly apparent that Stacie could not really understand how it was for her mom "back in the day."

This insight led Patti to work with her four co-authors to bring the memories and legacy of diploma school nursing to a wider audience. Through her career she has worked in intensive care, oncology and palliative care patient settings and as an instructor at Toledo Hospital School of Nursing where she met her co-authors.

In both her nursing and writing she hopes to help others and allow them to be heard. She is particularly proud of being part of the team to erect the BEFORE I DIE…board in the Toledo warehouse district and of writing with Beth White the *American Journal of Nursing* award winning *In the Shadows: Helping your Seriously Ill Adult Child*.

She and her husband Dan live in Toledo where they loved raising their two daughters. Her interests include enjoying family and friends, hiking, biking, and scrapbooking.

For **Susan J. Eisel**, participating in the writing this book on the history of diploma nursing education in Toledo with four wonderful nurse colleagues has been very special. Getting diploma nursing education "documented" was essential because it did happen and there are thousands of people in our Toledo community and elsewhere who benefitted from the kind hands and warm hearts of these nurses.

Eisel

It was enlightening, interesting and at times entertaining, to talk to nurses who openly shared meaningful stories about their diploma nursing education. Hearing their stories helped me reflect on my own story of becoming a nurse. Why? Because I am an "accidental nurse." I was not one of those nurses who could say "I always wanted to be a nurse." I always wanted to be a journalist, going into war zones, capturing the story of those in the trenches and reporting out the story for millions to read. I envisioned excitement, travel, journeys and adventures with a career in journalism. That dream started in 1970 but in 1974 I dropped out of my university studies in journalism, bewildered as to what to do next. It was in 1974 that I became "a nurse by accident." After leaving the university, my late aunt, Mary Lou French Yetis, RN, Toledo Hospital School of Nursing class of 1956, asked me one day, "What are you going to do? Have you considered nursing school?" I thought about her question, and then visited Flower Hospital School of Nursing, where she was nursing faculty, in July 1974. After touring and interviewing and being accepted, I matriculated in August 1974. My nursing career started by fate. I owe my aunt all my gratitude for opening my eyes to school, but also being a tireless cheerleader who always told me, "You can do this."

I consider myself very blessed to have enjoyed such a rich, wonderful career that has given me the excitement, allowed me to develop my compassion for others, and helped feed my soul by helping others. I have worked in Emergency Rooms, (my all time favorite patient care area), Intensive care areas, in hospital management, and nursing education. By far the most rewarding part of my career has been as a faculty teaching student nurses. For over 20 years I have met and hopefully helped many other young people meet their life goals of becoming a nurse. Working alongside student nurses is rewarding as well as challenging and the ultimate reward is watching that nursing student receive his or her nursing pin, surrounded by proud and loving family and friends. Being a part of that nursing faculty team that helps that student achieve his or her dream is both a humbling and joyful experience.

Many thanks to all who helped me succeed in my nursing career, negotiating and mastering my studies, molding me to be able to "think like a nurse," mentoring me as a new "staff or floor" nurse, new nurse faculty, or new nurse manager.

Maria Nowicki has lived and practiced in northwest Ohio throughout her career. A 1970 graduate of the Mercy Hospital School of Nursing, she received her Bachelor in Nursing degree from the University of Toledo. She received a Masters in Science and Education in Public Health and a PhD in Health Education from UT. Her Masters in Nursing is from Madonna University in Livonia, Mich.

Nowicki

Serendipity played a big part in her move from hospital practice to nursing education. In 1980, while taking classes to prepare for a supervisory position she was considering, a friend from her BSN study group told her about an open position at Toledo Hospital School of Nursing.

Looking back, Maria regards it as "the best move ever." She spent the next 33 years teaching first level nursing at both Mercy School of Nursing and The Toledo Hospital School of Nursing and eventually heading the nursing program at Mercy College of Ohio.

In the words of Michelangelo, she feels: "I am still learning." In retirement, her learning takes a different direction and she explores more of the creative talents of nurses – needlework, pottery, watercolor painting, jewelry making, and any other thing she sees that makes her say "I want to do that." Nursing has been an amazing career choice with many benefits, one of the best being the opportunity to meet her co-authors.

Encouraged by her mother, **Judy Harris Szor** was accepted into The Toledo Hospital School of Nursing after finishing high school. She began her nursing career in 1966 at The Toledo Hospital working in staff and then head nurse positions before she was recruited for the faculty of the Toledo Hospital School of Nursing in 1971. She has especially fond memories of her 17 years on the faculty, the last three of which were as assistant director. During these

Szor

years, she earned a BSN from the University of Michigan and an MEd from University of Toledo.

Following closure of the school of nursing in 1988, she continued at Toledo Hospital leading the first nurse residency orientation program for new graduates, followed by serving as the HIV/AIDs resource for the hospital, and eventually settling into an area of great interest to her, the role of Wound, Ostomy, Continence Nurse, a specialty in which she had become certified.

While in this role, she earned an MSN at Medical College of Ohio and also became certified as a Clinical Nurse Specialist, qualifying her as an Advanced Practice Nurse She left the hospital in 2001 to set up her own consulting business called Healing Wound and Ostomy Services, LLC, providing services to a large territory surrounding Toledo. The business allowed her the opportunity to experience nursing in a variety of settings including hospice and home care, long-term care, group homes and acute and subacute facilities.

She ended her business late in 2010 to be home with her ailing husband, but with some improvement in his health, returned to a part-time position in Healing Care at Hickman Cancer Center at Flower Hospital. As a Certified Healing Touch practitioner she provided healing touch, guided imagery and relaxation therapy to patients. She retired fully in 2015 and is now enjoying time with family and friends, traveling, playing piano, gardening, yoga, ballroom dancing and working on special projects.

She looks back over her career with a great sense of appreciation for being able to contribute in such meaningful ways, and encourages anyone so inclined to consider nursing. It is a most worthy and rewarding career.

Beth Heinzeroth White graduated from St. Vincent Hospital School of Nursing in 1973. Two years after graduating, while working in adult critical care, Beth received a Bachelor of Science in Nursing degree from Madonna College in Livonia, Mich. In 1981, she obtained a Master of Science in Nursing from Medical College of Virginia/Virginia Commonwealth University, Richmond, Virginia.

Her career spanned adult critical care to nursing care of children and perinatal nursing care. She has taught nursing at Toledo area diploma, ASN and BSN programs. Beth is a certified Pediatric Clinical Nurse Specialist and has a special interest in developmental pediatrics, particularly care of children with spina bifida.

White

This is her second published book. In 2013, she and Patricia Ringos Beach co-authored *In the Shadows: How to Help Your Seriously Ill Adult Child. In the Shadows* was awarded the 2013 ANA Book of the Year in the Consumer Health category.

Beth is now semi-retired and is working as a quality improvement consultant with the Ohio Perinatal Quality Collaborative.

Appendix
Record of Interviews

Adamczak, Barbara Halpin, St. Vincent Hospital School of Nursing, Class of 1958 – Written interview, Nov. 13, 2015.

Andrews, Mary Griffiths, University of Toledo Community Technical College, Class of 1987 – Interviewed by P. Beach, S. Eisel, J. Szor, and B. White, June 8, 2016.

Annesser, Carol C., Mercy Hospital School of Nursing, Class of 1980 – Mail interview/survey with M. Nowicki.

Anthony, Joanna Grilli, Maumee Valley Hospital School of Nursing, Class of 1967 – Interview J. Szor, Nov. 2, 2016.

Arquette, Mary Ann Shea, St. Vincent Hospital School of Nursing, Class of 1942 – Interview P. Beach, Aug. 6, 2015; Oct. 15, 2015.

Beam, Mary Depner, Flower Hospital School of Nursing, – Social Media

Bee, Sharon, Toledo Hospital School of Nursing, Class of 1977 – Interview B. White, Sep. 23, 2016.

Bersticker, Anita Boardman, Flower Hospital School of Nursing – Social Media

Bishop, Kathy Curley, Mercy Hospital School of Nursing, Class of 1967 – Email interview J. Szor, Aug. 23, 2016.

Borgelt, Bonnie Hummel, Flower Hospital School of Nursing, Class of 1974 – Interview S. Eisel, Sep. 29, 2016.

Brehm, Lissa Wilhelm, St. Vincent Hospital School of Nursing, Class of 1995 – Interview B. White, July 9, 2016.

Breitfelder, Michelle Beavers, Flower Hospital School of Nursing, – Social Media

Calabrese, Alice U., St. Vincent School of Nursing, Class of 1950 – Interview P. Beach, Oct. 6, 2016.

Choate, Sandy Coldiron, Flower Hospital School of Nursing – Social Media

Christian, Karen Steinmetz, Maumee Valley Hospital School of Nursing, Class of 1968 – Email interview J. Szor, July 22, 2016.

Cook, Janice Smith, Flower Hospital School of Nursing, Class of 1976 – Interview P. Beach, July 13, 2016.

Cygnor, Anita Kowaski, Mercy Hospital School of Nursing, Class of 1991 – Interview B. White, July 14, 2016.

Dillon, Victoria Vaughn, Flower Hospital School of Nursing, – Social Media

Drewyor, Glenda, Flower Hospital School of Nursing, Class of 1969 – Social Media

Drouillard, Jeanne Ann Calabrese, Mercy Hospital School of Nursing, Class of 1983 – Interview P. Beach, Oct.18, 2016.

Duerk, Alene, Toledo Hospital School of Nursing, Class of 1941 – Interview P. Beach & B. White, Aug.17, 2016.

Ellis-Moore, Elizabeth, Flower Hospital School of Nursing, Class of 1964 – Social Media, Aug. 15, 2014.

Felton, Pat Yancy, St. Vincent Hospital School of Nursing – Interview P. Beach (undated)

Firstenberger, Martha Cook, Toledo Hospital School of Nursing, Class of 1966 – Interview J. Szor, June 13, 2016.

Foos, Sue, Flower Hospital School of Nursing – Social Media

Fritz, Debbie, Flower Hospital School of Nursing – Social Media

Fry, Joyce, Riverside Hospital School of Nursing, Class of 1965 – Mail interview/survey with M. Nowicki

Graves, Mary Ann, Flower Hospital School of Nursing – Social Media

Gullberg, Ann Richardson, Flower Hospital School of Nursing – Social Media, Oct. 26, 2016.

Haberkamp, Rebecca Rayle, Flower Hospital School of Nursing – Social Media

Hallett, Annette Mazzurco, Mercy Hospital School of Nursing, Class of 1984 – Interview P. Beach, Sept. 27, 2016.

Hetherwick, Elaine Studer, Maumee Valley Hospital School of Nursing, Class of 1966 – Interview B. White, Aug. 9, 2016.

Holloway, Sandra Franklin, Toledo Hospital School of Nursing, Class of 1966 – Interview J. Szor, Sept. 10, 2016.

Horner, Catherine VanVorce, Flower Hospital School of Nursing, Class of 1969 – Interview B. White, Sept. 28, 2016; Social Media

Jaworski, Cathy Frame, Toledo Hospital School of Nursing, Class of 1981 – Interview B. White, July 7, 2016.

Jeffrey, Gayle, Mercy Hospital School of Nursing, Class of 1968 – Mail interview/survey with M. Nowicki.

Knoblauch, Diane, Toledo Hospital School of Nursing, Class of 1976 – Interview B. White, Nov. 3, 2016

Krill, Mary Unger, Flower Hospital School of Nursing – Social Media

Krochmalny, Barbara Rule, Flower Hospital School of Nursing – Social Media, Sept. 28, 2016.

Lake, Norma Provencher, St. Vincent Hospital School of Nursing, Class of 1974 – Interview B. White, July 8, 2016.

Langel, Lynn Kitchen St. Vincent Hospital School of Nursing, Class of 1974 – Interview P. Beach, June 30, 2016.

Layman, Naomi Crow (Marion), Flower Hospital School of Nursing – Social Media

Lemon, Betty Spencer, St. Vincent Hospital School of Nursing, Class of 1958 – Interview P. Beach, Nov. 13, 2015.

Lohmeyer, Sandra Frye Eastep, Flower Hospital School of Nursing, Class of 1964 – Social Media, Aug. 15, 2014.

Lucas, Linda Graver, Toledo Hospital School of Nursing, Class of 1984 – Interview P. Beach & B. White, Aug. 11, 2015.

Lycan, Jeff, Toledo Hospital School of Nursing, Class of 1984 – Interview P. Beach & B. White, Sept. 7, 2016.

Mackey, Loretta, Flower Hospital School of Nursing, Class of 1964 – Social Media, Aug. 15, 2014.

Maltman, Sue, Flower Hospital School of Nursing, Class of 1964 – Social Media, Sept. 28, 2016.

Meinen, Marilyn, Flower Hospital School of Nursing, Class of 1956 – Interview S. Eisel, Oct. 2016

Miller, Alice, Toledo Hospital School of Nursing, Class of 1941 – Interview P. Beach & J. Szor, Sept. 26, 2016.

Moellman, Barbara and Toledo Hospital School of Nursing Class of 1960 lunch bunch, Toledo Hospital School of Nursing, Class of 1960 – Interview J Szor, May 25, 2016.

Moore, Lois, Flower Hospital School of Nursing, Class of 1964 – Social Media, Aug. 15, 2014

Owen, Suzanne Mary Alexander, St. Vincent Hospital School of
Nursing, Class of 1974 – Interview P. Beach & B. White, Dec. 2,
2016.

Pirwitz, Sandy Crunkilton, Maumee Valley Hospital School of Nursing,
Class of 1968 – Email interview, J. Szor, July 27, 2016.

Quay, E. Wanda Foltz, Robinwood Hospital School of Nursing, Class of
1948 – Interview J. Szor & B. White, June 10, 2016.

Renton, Hope J. Wyse, Maumee Valley Hospital School of Nursing,
Class of 1968 – Email interview, J. Szor, Aug. 4, 2016.

Rolan, OdetteAnn Leininger, Flower Hospital School of Nursing, Class
of 1964 – Social Media, Aug. 15, 2014.

Root, Mary Findlay, Robinwood Hospital School of Nursing, Class of
1943 – Interview B. White, Nov. 3, 2016.

Scouten, Luanne Abel, Flower Hospital School of Nursing, – Social
Media

Shaw, Linda, St. Vincent Hospital School of Nursing, Class of 1974 –
Interview S. Eisel, Sept. 29, 2016.

Singer, Carol Manley, Toledo Hospital School of Nursing, Class of
1961– Interview B. White, Feb. 21, 2017

Smith, Amy, St. Vincent Hospital School of Nursing, Class of 1994 –
Interview P. Beach, S. Eisel & J. Jameson, Aug. 9, 2016

Smith, Lois Anspach, Toledo Hospital School of Nursing, Class of 1944
– Interview B. White, Feb. 25, 2017.

Snyder, Luann Schuerman, Ohio State University, Class of 1979 –
Interview P. Beach, S. Eisel, J. Szor, & B. White, June 8, 2016.

Surratt, Christine, Flower Hospital School of Nursing, Class of 1971 –

Social Media Oct. 29, 2016.

Swartz, Nancy R., Riverside Hospital School of Nursing, Class of 1959
– Email interview, June 6, 2016.

Tangeman, Janette Kish, Flower Hospital School of Nursing, Class of
1964 – Social Media, Aug. 15, 2014.

Tucker, Mary Margraf, St. Vincent Hospital School of Nursing, Class of
1973 – Interview B. White, July 11, 2015.

VanEtten, Kathleen Beck, Flower Hospital School of Nursing – Social
Media.

Viers, Sharon Kitchen, Mercy Hospital School of Nursing, Class of 1966
– Interview J. Szor, Oct. 6, 2016.

Wagonlander, Sheila, Flower Hospital School of Nursing, Class of 1952
– Interview P. Beach, S. Eisel & J. Jameson, Aug. 9, 2016.

Wasserman, Sr. Rita Mary, Mercy Hospital School of Nursing, Class of
1952– Interview M. Nowicki, Feb. 22, 2017.

Welsh, Carolyn Horn, Toledo Hospital School of Nursing, Class of
1966 – Interview J. Szor, Sept. 10, 2016.

Whitmore, Virginia Williams, Lucas County Hospital School of
Nursing, Class of 1943 –Interview B. White, Aug. 1, 2016.

Wilhelm, Beth Kaltenbach, St. Vincent Hospital School of Nursing,
Class of 1973 – Interview B. White, June 30, 2016.

Wilson, Kaye Lani Rae Rafko, St. Vincent Hospital School of Nursing,
Class of 1985 – Interview B. White, Nov. 9, 2016.

Young, Jan Sopher, Toledo Hospital School of Nursing, Class of 1967 –
Interview J. Szor, Oct. 20, 2016.

Zak, Cassandra Willey, Toledo Hospital School of Nursing, Class of
1972 – Interview B. White, July 11, 2016.

Index

Index

Division of Nurse Education ... 28 and 62
Dix, Dorothea ... 5
Dock, Lavinia L. ... 14, 19-21, 37, 39, and 40
dorm ... 35, 54, 85-103, 105-108, 111-113, 117, 118, 122, 138, 163, 184, 219, 222, 223, and 230
dormitory (see dorm)
dress code ... 103-105
Drewyor, Glenda ... xvii, 50, and 254
Drouillard, Jeanne Ann Calabrese ... xvii, 201, and 254
Duerk, Alene ... xvii, 47, 138, 183, 203-209, and 254

Eakins, Thomas ... 4
Eisel, Susan J. ... 129, 141, 143, 248, and 249
Ellis-Moore, Elizabeth ... xvii and 254

faculty ... xiii, 3, 37, 54, 57, 59, 70, 80, 86, 104, 117, 125, 127, 129, 131, 133, 136, 139-145, 152, 157, 173, 201, 212, 216, 225, and 248-250
Felton, Pat Yancy ... xvii and 254
feminism ... 13, 14, 19, 21, and 34
Firstenberger, Martha Cook ... xvii, 85, 114, 117, and 254
Flower Hospital School of Nursing ... xii, 43, 45, 47-50, 55, 58, 63, 64, 72, 78, 89, 90, 95, 96, 101, 103, 104, 107, 111, 112, 114, 116, 124, 129, 141, 143, 154, 158, 162, 179, 181, 207, 230, 231, and 248
Foos, Mary Lou ... 170
Foos, Sue ... xvii and 255
Fritz, Debbie ... xvii, 49, and 255
Fry, Joyce ... xvii and 255

Gilded Age ... 8
Goldmark Report ... 23, 24, 29, 33, and 109
Goldmark, Josephine ... 23, 24, and 29
Goodrich, Annie ... 24
Grace Hall ... 89
grading ... 26, 144, and 145
graduation ... 43, 46, 54, 64, 74, 76, 79, 107, 112, 113, 116, 120, 133, 152, 156, 187, 188, 189, 197, 201, 214, 219, 221-223, 228, 230, 231, 233, 235, 236, and 238
Graves, Mary Ann ... xvii, 48, and 255
Great Depression ... 25, 26, 27, 36, 49, 58, and 214
Gregory, Lindsay ... xvi
Gregory, Mary Booker ... xvii, 215, 217, and 218
Gross, Samuel D. ... 4, 5, and 6
Gullberg, Ann Richardson ... xvii and 255